Drug abuse in Ireland today is a frightening problem. But this is not a frightening book. Instead, it is factual, reassuring, and practical. James Comberton gives a realistic picture of the Irish drug scene, the life of the drug addict, the dead-end values and the special jargon of the drug culture. He shows how young people are caught up in the web of drug abuse, and he shows how they can escape, with your help.

The book is full of sound advice on all points, like what to do when faced with an overdose emergency, and how to organise community action against drugs. But it also has a deeper dimension. James Comberton believes that drugs, which offer young people the promise of freedom, really inflict the worst kind of repression — repressing the inevitable problems of growing up and facing life. Parents need to help their children to real independence. The chapters on parent effectiveness and communication within the family will repay careful reading, and may help towards a more thoughtful and open relationship between adults and young people.

DRUGS
and
young people

James Comberton

**WARD
RIVER
PRESS**

A Paperback Original
First published 1982 by
Ward River Press Ltd.,
Knocksedan House,
Swords, Co. Dublin, Ireland

ISBN O 907085 37 7

NOTE: While the information contained in this book has
been compiled with care, neither the author nor the pub-
lisher can accept liability for any misinformation or out-
of-date information contained therein. You are advised
to seek competent professional guidance before embark-
ing on any course of action outlined in this book.

Cover design by Steven Hope
Typeset by Inset Ltd.
Printed by Cahill Printers Limited,
East Wall Road, Dublin 3.

James Comberton is Executive Chairman of Coolemine Lodge Therapeutic Community, a residential, drug free programme for the rehabilitation of drug addicts. He introduced the Coolemine Parents Action and Prevention Programme to help parents to help themselves in combating drug abuse in Ireland.

Educated at Synge Street, Christian Brothers School, he is also a graduate of University College Dublin. Following a career in journalism, he entered communication consultancy and in time included organisational development. Subsequently, he studied Gestalt orientated psychotherapy and practices group psychotherapy at St. Patrick's Hospital.

He devised and conducted Assertion Training and Personal Development Workshops.

He has been Chairman of Coolemine Lodge since 1974 and is a member of the Board of Directors of the World Federation of Therapeutic Communities, and the European Federation of Therapeutic Communities.

CONTENTS

Preface

If you read all of this book you will learn a great deal about how young people can be drawn into experimenting with drugs, and how many of them lose control over their lives as they sink deeper into the drug sub-culture. You may be shocked by what can befall these youngsters who become addicted and what can happen to their families. It is right that you should know the facts about the drug hazard in our society.

But there is another more important message in this book. It is that you are not helpless. You can take effective action against the spread of drugs, and against the drug problem entering your home. In these pages you will find out what you can do and how you can do it.

I have aimed this book at parents because I believe that only parents are in a position to take the action necessary to at least curb our current drug problem. In fact, I believe that they can achieve a great deal more.

If parents take early, effective action, cannabis smoking and underage drinking, often the drugs of entry into the drug scene, can be substantially curtailed and the progression to stronger drugs and dependance stopped. Even more important, the development of young teenagers during this crucial growing and maturing phase of their lives will not be interrupted, or arrested, by the use of cannabis and/or other drugs.

The steps I describe apply particularly to youngsters of 12 to 16 years of age, the group currently most at risk. Parents can apply the steps to the extent and with the degree of intensity that suits them and their circumstances.

This book advocates taking a strong stand against drugs since experience with the terrible effects of drugs on youngsters demonstrates again and again that the easy way, or the 'hope for the best' attitude, will not match the influence and power of drugs. In this crisis, youngsters need parents who will stand firm. The action taken by parents must be based on love and concern, discipline, and respect for their youngsters, who have a right to expect responsible guidance and protection from drugs. The belief that "it could not happen to my child" is self-deluding and can only be held by those who are ignorant of the facts of the present situation. Such parents are hazards to their own children and are very much a part of the drug problem.

I have watched the growth in the numbers of drug taking youngsters, and consequent addiction for many of them, and its spread almost unimpeded in Dublin and into other parts of the country. I do not accept that it is inevitable or that it cannot be stopped. It can.

The Coolemine Parents Action and Prevention Programme, devised with this in mind, is based on the action of American parents and our needs here in Ireland. It also draws on the experience of parents and relatives who are members of the Coolemine Family and Friends Association who have drug abusers and addicts in their families. As well, it is based on a knowledge of drug abusers and drug dependants, their thinking and behaviour, and the paths they follow into addiction. This book gives details of that programme as well as much other material on prevention.

Parents are not helpless in this situation. They have more power and influence than they realise. Collectively, they can make the difference in tackling this problem. This book is designed to equip parents with the knowledge they need and shows them how they can take effective steps to combat drug abuse. If they don't who else will?

I would like to express my gratitude to members of the National Federation of Parents for Drug-free Youth in the U.S.A. for the material they have so generously shared. I am also grateful to Msgr. William O'Brien, President of Daytop Village, New York, and the staff of that great therapeutic community for their ongoing interest in and co-operation with Coolemine Lodge Therapeutic Community. Without this fraternal association I might not have encountered the American parents' movement.

I would also like to acknowledge the contribution of the dedicated staff of Coolemine Lodge in developing and launching the Parents Action and Prevention Programme. In particular I must mention the invaluable contribution by the Director

Tom McGarry. The presentation of elements of Parent Effectiveness Training by Mary Ellen McCann made the task of compiling the 'Communicating with your Child' so much easier. I must make special mention of the tireless members of the Coolemine Family and Friends Association and their President, Ms. Peggy Meany, for their dedication and commitment to fighting the spread of drug abuse, and their courage in publicly sharing their experiences of drug addiction in their homes.

Thanks are also due to the Lions Club of Dundrum and Leopardstown for taking up the work. The parents of Grange, Dublin who have creatively and with thorough preparation launched the first Parents Action and Prevention community programme, deserve special mention. Their pioneering work will bring benefits to a great many parents and inspire many more.

We have been losing the battle against drugs. The threat to Irish youngsters intensifies every day. It needn't be that way. Parents can turn the tide — individually, and working together.

James Comberton

Chapter 1
Introduction

Drug abuse has reached serious proportions in Dublin, and it has penetrated to Cork, Limerick, Galway and even small towns around the country. Since early 1979, the drug abuse problem has virtually exploded in our society. Perhaps the most sinister development has been the spread of addiction to the very young, the children between the ages of 12 to 15 years. The implication of this development in a society where the majority of the population are very young people is all too obvious.

The response of parents has, understandably, been one of puzzlement and fright, and in some cases, unfortunately, denial of the reality of illegal drugs. Parents have found themselves in a position of having to respond to entirely new circumstances without any guidelines, without a knowledgeable and supportive community, without their own parents to serve as models for them. They have had no experience of, or preparation for, this unique problem.

And where exactly is the threat? It lies in the new phenomenon, the sinister drug environment which has seeped into all levels of our society. It is now impossible for a youngster to get through his or her teens without encountering pressure to use drugs. Youngsters are under pressure to experiment and use drugs at parties, discos, in pubs, in schools, wherever youngsters congregate, even on the playing fields. There is a plentiful supply of drugs, relatively easy to obtain and plenty of users to encourage others, and the opportunities. Older boys and girls often introduce the younger ones to alcohol and drugs. Remember that drug addicts create addicts. The "pusher" is probably a young person, who is using drugs; it could be a boy or girl next door. In the worst possible situation, it could be your son or daughter. For some unfortunate parents whom I have met, this is a reality.

We have waited too long in responding to the situation, and we have been losing the battle, offering virtually no community resistance to the spread of drug abuse. It has been with us for the past 15 years, growing in intensity. Like other countries we have called for the institutional answers — more garda activity, legislation and calls for education in the schools. The fact is that drug abuse is mainly a psycho-social problem and can only be solved by parents in their homes, and in their own neighbourhood, or in co-operation with schools. Of course we need more comprehensive laws, more effective courts, vigorous law enforcement and appropriate education in schools. These are a necessary part of the solution. But getting drugs out of the fabric of our society is a task only parents can perform by vigilance in the home, and prompt action, and by parents acting together.

Despite what you may have believed over the

past few years, parents are not helpless. You don't have to sit idly by while your children are drawn into the drug culture. You can make a difference. Out of love and concern for your own children, your neighbour's youngsters, and the young people in your community, you can reach out to other parents and concerned adults and, together, create a drug free environment for your children to grow up in. Youngsters have a right to this protection.

Law enforcement is but one of three approaches to combating drugs, the other two being treatment or rehabilitation, and prevention. The National Drugs Advisory and Treatment Centre, Jervis Street Hospital, provides medical and assessment service including detoxification for all age groups, as well as counselling and advisory services for both youngsters and parents. Coolemine Lodge Therapeutic Community provides a rehabilitation programme for over-18s. Unfortunately, there are no residential rehabilitation facilities for those of age 13 to 18 who have become dependant on drugs and in need of more intensive treatment. Coolemine Lodge Therapeutic Community is endeavouring to get the support necessary to open a facility appropriate for these youngsters.

However successful the Drug Squad and the Garda Task Force become, I think that we can expect the illegal import of drugs to continue in some quantities into the foreseeable future. Prevention, therefore, is the major area of endeavour remaining which has yet to be fully actioned. A necessary aspect of prevention is removing drug abusers and addicts from the drug scene, preferably to rehabilitate them, but removing them where possible from their criminal activities such as breaking and entering. While in circulation they "infect" other youngsters and expand the drug problem.

It is in this area that there has been a great lack of understanding. It is said in some quarters, that the problem is not as bad as it is being made out to be, that the problem is small or of moderate proportions. This ignores the obvious fact about drugs. Whatever the size of the problem now, it is going to get steadily worse in time unless comprehensive measures are taken to curb and reduce it. The face is, of course, that we already have a serious problem. This is the reality. At a certain moment, I believe a society passes the point of no return in the level of drug abuse and addiction. I believe that we have not reached this point yet, though I cannot prove it. But if we fail to rise to the challenge now, the opportunity to beat drugs will have passed and we can settle down to living with a high level of drug addiction, violence and other crimes which we are already experiencing. The fact that such a high percentage of our population is made up of young people makes us uniquely vulnerable.

In this situation, only parents can meet and beat drugs. And to do it they need to be well informed, know what they can do individually and collectively, and how they can do it.

The fact that parents usually know little or

nothing about drugs of abuse tends to make them feel helpless. They have had no training for this. In many ways the drugs themselves are almost irrelevant though it is helpful to be knowledgeable about them. What a parent does need to know is as much as possible about the behaviour of experimenters, drug abusers, and drug dependant people, or if you like, addicts, and what to do about it! There is no great mystery about this. Parents are experts on their own home and children, and on the local community. With this knowledge they can learn in the following pages what they can do and how to do it, and how to use the resources available when they need them.

Why do youngsters abuse drugs?
There are a great many theories but few agreed answers. Amongst the obvious possibilities that are suggested are unemployment, bad housing and other social and economic factors but though they may contribute it is not that simple since drug addiction is affecting all sectors of our society.

There are social, psychological, physiological, many contributory factors and influences. Drugs are available, and plentiful, and there is pressure to use them. Drugs are often used by youngsters to avoid handling day to day problems. Unfortunately, escaping through the use of drugs during adolescence means that the person doesn't develop the resources, the habit, or the capacity to face life's problems. If he fails to cope with frustration and other difficulties, simple problems assume gigantic proportions in his mind. Escaping this way also interferes with natural growth and changes during adolescence, and he is likely to emerge from adolescence not having matured emotionally or psychologically, feeling inadequate in an adult world.

Another contributing reason may be boredom and frustration. Life may not measure up to a youngster's fantasy ideal. Not having been facilitated to become self-starters and problem solvers, many young people lack the resourcefulness to seek out interests and things to do. They drift from one source of diversion and entertainment to another hoping to fill the void in their lives. Drugs are forbidden and therefore seemingly exciting — at the beginning. Other youngsters seek and experiment with new experiences and go after mind expansion and enhanced awareness. Others simply want to get high and feel "happy" by using mood altering drugs.

By far the strongest reason for entry into the drug scene is peer pressure, the most powerful force outside of the home. Peer pressure, that is pressure from other youngsters, together with the almost all-pervasive drug environment, are a real and potent threat to youngsters and the values and influence of the home. Smoking cannabis and drinking have become the things to do. Youngsters want to belong, to copy other youngsters, and it can lead them into trouble, particularly if there is one, or two, dominating and often older youngsters using drugs in their group who are admired and copied. Often these older youngsters feed young rebelliousness, and challenge others to live dangerously.

Availability of drugs and the ease with which they can be obtained are of course, prime factors. Dublin is the drug supply centre and has the greatest problem. The fact that drug addiction has spread to Cork, Galway, Limerick, Waterford and other cities, and is spreading to small towns, indicates how well established the distribution of illegal drugs has become, and how deeply they have become embedded in the fabric of our society.

In addition, our culture is drug orientated ("A pill for every ill") and the easy availability of drugs which are so readily used for even minor and transitory ailments has prepared the ground for the specific use of narcotics, and the consequent addiction to them by the emotionally troubled.

Even more important, our society has not developed norms for the moderate and social use of alcohol. We are polarised into total abstinence or careless and excessive consumption of alcohol. Youngsters learn early that it is acceptable to get "plastered" and that a "great night" means to get drunk. The "hard man" image, the person who can "put it away", far from being frowned on or deplored is seen to be accepted as a good fellow. Excessive drinking by parents is part of the experience of a significantly large number of addicted youngsters. The high level of alcohol addiction in our society has meant that we do not have an accepted model for responsible drinking. Our misguided approach to alcohol is also demonstrated in our courts, though now less frequently, where defendants can offer drunkenness as an acceptable defence.

Who becomes addicted?

It is impossible to say in advance who amongst the youngsters who experiment with drugs or join in groups smoking cannabis and drinking alcohol will advance to other drugs and become dependant.

It is reasonable to assume that the mood altering effect of drugs has a special significance for some youngsters. Their experience with cannabis, or alcohol, may give them a taste for mood altering drugs which lures them towards stronger drugs and greater highs and ultimate addiction.

Individuals experience the effects of drugs differently. A "high" for one youngster may mean that he also experiences a pleasurable release from symptoms of anxiety, tension and interpersonal stress which other youngsters do not experience, or at least not to the same degree. The absence of anxiety and stress and the experience of the "high" may attract the youngster to continue the use of drugs to obtain relief and consequently progress to stronger drugs, including heroin, and become dependant on them. It is certainly clear that drugs remove the individual from actuality. Detachment is one of the most frustrating characteristics of the drug dependent youngster.

At the same time, it must be recognised that all youngsters who suffer anxiety, tension and interpersonal stress do not automatically, or inevitably, become drug abusers. Those who do, we believe are suffering from a personality disorder. Unfortunately, there are no clear or easy answers in the area of drug dependance.

Whatever the reason, we can prevent the use of drugs and the consequent addiction of young people. We can reduce the drug risk in the environment in which our youngsters live by vigilance and parental action. We can also pay much more attention to increasing youngsters' ability to resist drugs by helping them to develop self-reliance and responsibility, by better preparation for life — and by our own example.

A youngster's drug or alcohol addiction can be much more overwhelming than adult alcoholism, though the ravages of their addiction can bring enough misery and devastation. First, it can take up to 15 years of drinking before the late stages of alcoholic behaviour manifest themselves. Drug addiction among youngsters develops much more rapidly, particularly in the case of heroin.

Second, the older alcoholic person will usually have built a family, a home, and has had reasonable successful job experience. He or she will want to hold onto these, or get them back. This provides him or her with powerful motivation to seek treatment, though not all will respond. The young addict has no such achievement behind him and therefore does not have this kind of motivation. In fact he is likely to reject these possibilities in his life as being too "straight".

Drug Sources
They are frequently purchased from friends and older youngsters who are often dependant on drugs. Drug addicts create addicts. The original source of illegal drugs are the "pushers" and "dealers". Other means of obtaining drugs are breaking into pharmacies and forging prescriptions. Drugs are also stolen in the home. They are often obtained through doctors who are known to give prescriptions on payment, and overprescribe. Drug abusers and addicts are also very persuasive and can manipulate or threaten some doctors into prescribing drugs for them. Parents are sometimes persuaded to collude with the youngster to obtain drugs.

Dependance on Drugs
Before dealing with prevention, I think that readers will benefit from a description of dependance and what can happen to a family, and a dependant person.

Dr. Daniel Casriel, a founder of Daytop Village, New York, the first therapeutic community for drug addicts, believes that there are four types, or degrees of addicts. "One is the pre-addict, the person who has a potential to be addicted and who, if set in an environment where there are drugs around, will become addicted. Then there is the fringe, or peripheral, addict. He is already 'nibbling', is already on some narcotic drug. He has a predisposition and, if allowed to continue, will develop an addiction. The third type is what I call the soft-core addict, who is taking heroin, but has been taking it for less than a year. He might have been arrested, he might have been in trouble. But his whole life doesn't *yet* centre around addiction. Finally, there is the hard-core addict, whose life has been totally centered around drug addiction for at least a year, and in most cases for several years."

The Addicted or Dependant Person

Let's look at the addicted person. He is addicted to a pharmacological substance. He is probably 17 years of age having begun experimenting at the age of 15. Today, many begin at 12, 13, 14 years of age. Like most others, he started with alcohol and then progressed to cannabis with the encouragement or insistence of his friends. Subsequently, he tried other drugs, perhaps cocaine too. At no stage did he believe that he was moving towards addiction. Eventually, he tried heroin and, not so gradually, he became addicted.

Meanwhile, his school performance deteriorated, he dropped sports, he began to look scruffy, slept a lot, became very demanding, had strange looking callers, and was very unsocial, often hostile, at home.

During this time he exhausted home as a source of money, having also stolen items from home to sell for drug money. He turned to stealing from others, forging cheques, burgling chemist shops and inevitably had run-ins with the law. Eventually, he raised enough money to purchase drugs, particularly heroin. He "cut" or diluted it with some solutions and started selling it to others. When he commenced it probably cost IR£3.00 for a gramme of cannabis but to keep himself supplied with heroin he needs anything from £70 to £120 per day depending on the stage of his addiction.

He is now a compulsive user of heroin and when this is not available, or money is scarce, he obtains substitute drugs, and may use them with alcohol. He has a repetitive craving for the heroin and cannot do without it. He is both physically and psychologically dependant on drugs.

The physical dependance varies with the drug and these are usually sedatives or opiates particularly heroin. The physical dependance can be relatively easily dealt with if he is willing to undergo detoxification. But the psychological dependance, the craving, is less easily dealt with.

Initially, the person pursues the particular pleasurable effects which he desires. But tolerance builds up and the person has to take increasing amounts to achieve even "normality". Gradually, the euphoric, pleasurable effect diminishes despite the use of ever larger amounts until he complains that he "gets" nothing out of it any more, but he believes with deep conviction that he must continue to take it to feel normal, to avoid suffering withdrawal symptoms, being sick, sweating, trembling, etc.

Persistent use of drugs, particularly heroin and barbiturates, exposes the person to great risks. He may very well "overdose" and die, or mix alcohol with other drugs particularly barbiturates, and perhaps suffocate through vomiting in his sleep. Drug addicts are prone to serious accidents when under the influence of drugs.

There may be a deterioration in his health, brain damage in severe cases, and of course hepatitis of the liver through the casual use of "infected" syringes.

The young person gradually loses his self-respect, becomes hostile towards society, and particularly towards his parents. He takes on a new identity, that of the drug addict. This in itself often gives him a justification for his future drug related activities. Almost all aspects of his life deteriorate and all his energies are devoted to getting drugs, or the money to purchase them. This inevitably leads him into crime and into contact with the law.

Addicts may be induced to go for treatment but they rarely have any real motivation. Their purpose is, more often than not, to obtain more drugs or to use treatment facilities to avoid the consequences of their activities, to avoid an impending court case or other undesirable consequences. Until the advent of the therapeutic community, traditional treatment approaches failed to rehabilitate the addict. The frustrating impenetrable detachment of the addicted person kept him impervious to standard clinical approaches, counselling and custodial treatment.

His lack of motivation and ruthless, purposeful exploitation of the people he encounters, including those who are clearly there to help him, makes him a very difficult person to help. But the situation is not hopeless. Coolemine Therapeutic community, which is run mainly by trained ex-addicts, provides a therapeutic environment where the afflicted person can recover his self-respect, and help himself by helping others.

In starting the process of his rehabilitation, his parents, or other pressures and influences, can direct him towards the National Drugs Advisory and Treatment Centre. Here he will be counselled and medically examined. It is more than likely that the addicted person is suffering from Hepatitis. If he is willing, and depending on the evaluation of the Centre, he can be detoxified there. He will also be put in contact with Coolemine Lodge. If he is less heavily addicted, he may be able to attend the Centre, and pursue a gradual withdrawal programme.

The Family's Dilemma

It is not unusual for parents to discover that their teenager has been using drugs, especially pot, for one, two, or even three years before they eventually find out. With hindsight, they can then often recognise subtle changes in behaviour which at the time they found troublesome or worrying, but which they tended to dismiss telling themselves that it was just adolescence, or that it was unfair not to be more trusting. Anyway, they reassured themselves that *their* child would never touch drugs, and were reluctant to create what might be needless fuss.

Understandably, parents are most reluctant to

think that their child could be abusing drugs and they are slow to recognise the signs which may not be all that obvious, bearing in mind the changes in mood and behaviour which parents expect in adolescence anyway.

Detecting drug use is also made very difficult for parents, particularly in the early stages, because drug abusers become expert in covering their activities and they may be able to retain some measure of control over a long period. Since they have no hesitation in lying, they can give very plausible and convincing explanations to their parents for their behaviour.

A typical case was Noreen, a 16 year old school-girl who was smoking pot (cannabis) regularly, and experimenting with other drugs for a year before her school teacher discovered it and informed her parents. Up till then she had never been a source of serious worry to her parents, was obedient and always came home in good time. Their biggest worry was that she went to discos where a group used drugs. Also, they were aware that she was friendly with several young people who used drugs.

Her parents considered their relationship with their daughter to be a close, loving one, with trust on both sides. They became deeply distressed and angry when they discovered that she had been lying to them. She had even ridiculed them for their "ridiculous suspicions" about her being drunk on a couple of occasions when in fact she had been "stoned" on pot. On reflection, her mother realised that there had been a change in her daughter's attitude to her and that she had not been as open and confiding as formerly. She also discovered that her school work had deteriorated very much during this period.

It was not until she was about two months drug-free that this girl began to change, and her attitude of detachment, as well as resentment and hostility following the discovery of her drug use, was replaced by a warmer, more open manner once again. Her interest in sport activities increased, her school work improved, and she became much happier.

This girl's parents took the steps suggested by the Coolemine Parents Action and Prevention Programme, and advocated in this book, and they were able to successfully rescue her from the drug environment in which she had allowed herself to become trapped.

Changes induced by pot smoking can be insidious and almost imperceptible. This is not so in the case of heroin where change can be very rapid once addiction sets in. Even here, parents can be fobbed off with lies by a son or daughter who may claim that he is "only" smoking pot, and insists that it is harmless. Clutching at straws, parents often delude themselves into believing this.

Often this fiction is maintained until the heroin addict succumbs to hepatitis (usually the result of using infected syringes) and becomes very jaundiced. Even then, many young addicts may continue to deny that they have a drug problem. Admission of a drug problem forces the addicted youngster to concede that he should do something about it, that is, obtain treatment. And, if he does not wish to take treatment, he has to change his "game"; he can no longer, however, deny his drug abuse, and he must face the open accusations and reproaches of his family.

At the same time, he may no longer take the trouble to hide his habit. He may become much more blatant in his behaviour and steal from other family members with impunity, and become aggressive and threatening when confronted.

A typical situation within the family of an 18 or 19 year old drug addict may involve a sister who is working and has had her money and valued possessions stolen from her by her addict brother. She may be frequently threatened or actually assaulted when she accuses him. Often in such situations she, rather than he, is sent away "for safety" to stay with another family member and to escape from the tension and conflicts caused by the addict's presence in the family. Other members of the family are often disadvantaged or penalised instead of the addict.

Families almost always come into conflict on the issue of whether the addict should ultimately be put out, or allowed to remain and continue to wreak havoc within the home. Mothers generally suffer most guilt at the prospect of expelling the addict son or daughter fearing, amongst other considerations, that he may be found dead following an overdose of drugs. Unfortunately, allowing the addict to remain at home, and providing him with food, shelter and, inevitably, money only prolongs his addiction, and deepens its hold on him. Nor is it any guarantee against a fatal over-dose. In fact, it increases his drug abuse since the money he saves on rent and food is spent on drugs.

Until the discomfort of being addicted becomes greater than the discomfort of undergoing treat-ment, the addicted person will not, cannot change. An actively addicted person is no longer in control of his behaviour — his addiction controls him. So until he is allowed to experience the reality of the consequences of his behaviour, and is not protec-ted or supported by the family, he is unlikely to find the motivation to change.

In the case of the under 18 age group, particular-ly those of 12 to 16 years, parents can generally do much more to rescue their child from the drug environment, and protect him from it, because he is still very much dependent on them emotionally and in every other way. It is usually possible to insist on behaviour which would not generally be feasible with over 18s.

When parents discover that a son or daughter has become addicted, the sooner they confront this problem the better, because it will not go away by itself, and it can only get worse. No amount of promises from an addict mean anything, and they are basically manipulations to enable him to con-tinue the "habit", no matter how sincere he may sound. Parents often clutch at worthless promises again and again, and may find themselves in serious conflict with each other. Some families do not recover from the conflicts, the recriminations and mutual hostility brought on by the drug problem of a youngster.

If an addict succeeds in getting one of the parents to collude with him, and more often than not he does succeed and generally it is his mother, she finds herself promising not to tell the father about money stolen, etc., and consequently a wedge is driven between them. Parents need to face up to the problem together no matter how fearful they may be of the consequences if they wish to give their addicted son or daughter the only real help they can offer at this stage — to induce them to go for treatment possibly under the threat of withdrawing all support if they refuse.

This approach may also need to extend to eventually refusing to bail the young person out of prison when he is once again in trouble with the law on drugs charges or drug related offences such as robbery, stealing, breaking and entering, etc. It is often only as a result of experiencing these realities that an addict becomes sick and tired of the consequences of his addiction and, knowing that he has nowhere else to run to, will probably reluctantly face up to dealing with his addiction.

It is essential that parents make it clear that it is because they love and care for their addicted young person that they refuse to continue to make it easier for him to destroy himself, and because they believe that with treatment he will recover, and that he has the power to do it. The problem belongs with the addicted person, and only he can decide whether he wants to recover or not. No one else can force him to do so, but they can help him by not colluding with him and by resisting his inevitable blackmail attempts, and thus enable him to seek help to commence recovery, if this is his choice.

Chapter 2
The truth about Cannabis

The widely held belief that cannabis is a harmless, non-addictive drug and the widespread ignorance of the dangers to youngsters of cannabis is alarming in our society. Parents report that counsellors and other adults in advisory positions have been telling them that cannabis is harmless and not to worry about it. This attitude to cannabis is particularly disturbing because this drug, and alcohol, are often the first drugs that youngsters experiment with. If we could prevent this first step we could do much to reduce drug abuse and addiction.

Most of the erroneous opinions expressed are echoes of ideas of the early '70s, before serious research got under way, and before we in Ireland had an opportunity to observe and become familiar with its damaging effects. The truth is that cannabis, also known as marijuana, pot and other names, is a very dangerous drug and can be responsible for damaging personality and physical changes in teenagers.

The effects of marijuana are not as dramatic, nor is it addictive like heroin, but marijuana is all the more deceptive and insidious because of this. Its effects develop so subtly and imperceptibly that it is difficult for others, including parents, to discern what is happening to the user until the drug has already begun to alter and damage him. Unfortunately, the user himself is also unaware of what is happening to him and often thinks that he has proof that cannabis is harmless. In addition, the person who continually uses marijuana may also develop a taste for the effect of the drug and is likely to progress to other drugs, including heroin, in search of greater "highs".

Part of the problem of recognising marijuana abuse is that many of the symptoms mimic difficult adolescence and include impaired performance, apathy, lack of interest, loss of motivation, and constantly feeling pressured. But young marijuana users gradually become more and more detached, concentration, memory and therefore learning is affected, school performance declines and the youngster begins to drop out. At this stage he is hard to reach. Probably one of the most alarming effects of cannabis on the young person is that it retards the maturation process. In other words, the youngster does not grow up as he should. The continuous use of alcohol has much the same effect on teenagers.

Adolescence is a time when young people are allowed to try new things, experiment with their talents, test their abilities, and hopefully assume new responsibilities. Young people need to experience and deal with loneliness, depression, sexual worries, frustration and the other emotions or situations that arise. If these experiences are dulled or avoided through the use of cannabis, alcohol or other drugs, the youngster does not grow or mature. The young person, who when thwarted, disappointed, frightened, insecure, or hurt, reaches for the now readily available cannabis joint, opts out and does not learn from his experiences.

The young person who takes the instant acceptance offered by the drug peer group, that is youngsters of his own age using drugs, rather than opting for the more challenging inclusion of his drug-free peers, takes the easy way into trouble.

At a time when youngsters are most in need of gaining and developing an adult approach in dealing with their own needs and the needs of others, they become more and more self-absorbed. When they should be developing the discipline that will enable them to defer or put off immediate pleasure, they revert to an almost infantile expectation of instant gratification. When they most need to consider long term goals, they are operating in a time-frame of days or even hours.

If we allow the present situation of widespread cannabis abuse and underage drinking to continue we will have, in time, an unmanageable number of emotionally, socially, or intellectually handicapped citizens to look after. We will have an increasing number of 20 to 30 year old early adolescents. This will be a tragedy, as well as being a burden on society.

Pharmacology
Cannabis Sativa (Marijuana) is a very complex

plant, consisting of some 421 chemicals. Of these, more than 60 are classified as cannabinoids. Four of the cannabinoids are known to be psychoactive (mind-altering), and the one we hear the most about is Delta-9-tetrahydrocannabinol, usually referred to as THC. THC is concentrated in the flowering tops of the marijuana plant, and its strength can range from 1% to 11% in the drug variety of the plant. The THC content in the plant is unstable, varying greatly with environmental factors such as heat and light.

A one-gram cannabis cigarette contains from 10 to 100 milligrams of THC. A five to ten milligram intake of THC into the bloodstream is sufficient to induce cannabis intoxication, or a "high".

In the early 1960s, the cannabis being smoked was of low potency, approximately .5% to 1% THC content. However, over the ensuing two decades, potency of the drug steadily increased until today, most street marijuana averages 4% to 6% THC content. The sinsemilla (seedless) has yielded a THC content as high as 11.08%. Increased THC contents are due primarily to advanced methods of cultivation.

Cannabis research is still in its infancy. THC was isolated in 1964, and a controlled quality THC (standardized dose) was only made available to research scientists as recently as 1969. It is very important to note that the THC content of this standardized cannabis (commonly referred to as the "NIDA Joint") is 2%.

Probably the most significant fact to remember

about the drug cannabis is that it is fat soluble. In that respect, it bears some similarity to the chemical DDT. The THC clings to the fatty tissues of the body, and repeated doses of the drug can result in accumulation of the THC in those fat cells of the body. For the sake of comparison, let's look at another drug — alcohol. If you take a drink of alcohol — or a few drinks — in 12 to 18 hours, all that alcohol will be metabolized out of your system. However, if you smoke a marijuana cigarette, 30% to 50% of the THC will still be in your body after one week, and it would take nearly three to four weeks to metabolize it thoroughly from your system. In other words, the high goes but the THC stays in the body.

It is cannabis's fat solubility that makes the drug a very serious health hazard, but the problem is further complicated because of the subtle nature of the drug.

Cannabis produces no obvious or readily recognisable reaction such as is found with most other drugs. There are very obvious signs of alcohol intoxication, such as vomiting, slurring of speech or staggering. PCP and LSD both have very dramatic and immediate results on the user, including hallucinations and bizarre behaviour. But, other than a reddening of the eyes, enlarged pupils, and a loss of facial flush, there are no other easily discernible symptoms of a cannabis "high". In addition, the accumulation of the THC in the body's fatty tissues occurs over a long period of time and is a gradual process. It is therefore difficult for other people to discern what is happening to the user until the drug has already begun to alter and damage him.

Health Hazards
The Brain
THC builds especially heavily in the brain, and studies by Dr. Robert Heath of Tulane University have indicated that it can cause structural changes in the synapses between the cells of the brain. It appears that some of these structural changes may be of a permanent nature.

Other studies (Gilkesen) done with deep sited encephalograms have shown disruptions in brain waves, with the chronic or long term cannabis, or pot, smokers exhibiting printouts similar to the learning disabled. The ability to make computations and do sequential functions is also affected. Cannabis also interferes with the individual's short term memory and his ability to process information into long term memory — which is learning — and which is a vital function for the school age youngster. Other effects of pot smoking are emotional flatness, diminished will power, concentration, attention span, tolerance for frustration, increased confusion in thinking, impaired judgement, hostility towards authority — and refusal to accept the facts about cannabis.

The Reproductive System
THC interferes with the pituitary gland's ability to produce hormones in both males and females.

While this might not prove such a critical problem in the fully developed adult, it is crucial for the maturing adolescent who is going through puberty.

In males, there has been found a reduction of up to 44% in production of the principal male hormone, testosterone. During the period of puberty, young men receive a surge of testosterone, and heavy and prolonged marijuana use during this time, can result in what is now being clinically referred to as "arrested pubertal development". These young men are not experiencing muscle development, growth, and the development of secondary sexual characteristics that are associated with puberty.

Such a young man would have a kind of uni-sex look, with narrow shoulders, very little muscle, concave chest, pale complexion, small in size and pants kind of hanging on the tailbone.

Cannabis smokers are also more likely to have reduced sperm count, less active sperm and more abnormal sperm than do non-smokers. No actual research is done with women of child bearing age; however, studies have been conducted using rhesus monkeys instead, which are as close to the human body as possible in the animal kingdom (28 day ovulatory cycle). One such study reports that 44% of all offspring conceived by THC (2%) treated female monkeys resulted in spontaneous abortion, fetal death, or stillbirth. When the THC dose was doubled, the death rate doubled as well.

Cannabis accumulates in the female ovaries as well as other organs and also affects the female ovulation cycle and there is need to be concerned when one remembers that a female's egg supply is there for life. If they are damaged, there is no way to repair the injury. THC also passes the placental barrier to the growing fetus, and will pass through the mother's milk to a nursing infant. Dr. Gabriel Nahes of Columbia University College of Physicians discovered that THC exposure diminished the capacity of individual cells to arrange life according to the genetic plan built into cellular molecules. THC inhibits formation of DNA (essential for correct cell functioning and division) in cells, resulting in cellular death and abnormality.

The Lungs

Most people today are very aware of the deleterious effects of cigarettes and tobacco on the respiratory system of the body and the resultant health hazards that tobacco smoking causes. It is therefore of great concern to discover that cannabis produces 50% more tar than the equivalent weight of tobacco. In addition, the cannabis tar contains from 50% to 100% more carcinogens, or cancer-producing agents (such as benzolapyrene).

One cannabis joint is equivalent to a pack of tobacco cigarettes in terms of the damage done to the air passages of the lungs. In recent studies done on American soldiers in Germany — young men who had been smoking cannabis on a daily basis for one or two years — lung damage and precancerous lesions were present that are usually associated with heavy tobacco smokers after 20 or 30 years.

Unfortunately, many cannabis smokers couple their practice with tobacco smoking as well, increasing the likelihood of lung problems. Further damaging the respiratory system is the manner in which cannabis is smoked. The joint is smoked down to the very end because the expense prompts total use of the substance and there is a greater concentration of the drug in the butt of the joint. The butt also has more tars. In addition, the cannabis is inhaled deeply into the lungs and held there in order to produce a greater high.

The Immune Response System

Cannabis reduces the body's ability to produce the white blood cells that fight invasion of the body by outside agents such as viruses and bacteria. A heavy user might have difficulty in fighting off infections and also might be more susceptible to colds and flus.

The Cardiovascular System

Cannabis can increase the heart beat up to 50%, a particularly dangerous consequence for anyone who has heart disease or impairment.

Marijuana and Driving

We can expect more traffic *fatalities* due to cannabis intoxication. Cannabis affects peripheral vision, performance, and reaction time of a driver. Stoned drivers have a distorted sense of time, and the effects on driving may last long past smoking the joint. When you remember that cannabis is frequently used with alcohol you realise that the combination results in a very disorientated driver who is a very high risk to himself and other road users.

Much more can be said about the dangers of using cannabis. It is obvious that parents must take a strong stand on the use of this drug, and alcohol. As stated at the beginning of this chapter, if parents can stop pot smoking and underage drinking particularly in the early teenage years, much of the subsequent drug abuse can be avoided. But protecting youngsters from the dangers of cannabis itself would be a major achievement.

Chapter 3
How to Protect your Home

What can you do to protect your home?

There are a number of approaches to protecting the home from the ever-present threat of drugs. I will try to cover some of the factors and the influences that should help to strengthen the central position and influence of the home.

Obviously, parents should discuss drugs and the drug scene with their children not, of course, as an isolated subject but as part of ongoing discussions on matters relating to, and of interest to, the youngster. However, in order to discuss drugs and the drug scene you need to know something of drugs; otherwise your opinions may be dismissed with typical adolescent contempt. To help you, detailed information on common drugs of abuse is provided in Chapter 12. These discussions should reveal your firm stand on drugs, including alcohol, and your reasons for this stand.

Youngsters often challenge parents with their own drinking and cigarette smoking and this should give parents pause for thought. However, remember that the effects of drugs, alcohol and cannabis, are quite different for adults and growing, developing youngsters. Excessive adult drinking cannot be justified, nor of course can the use of

cannabis by adults be anything but foolish and misguided, and illegal. For the adolescent youngster,
these drugs can be disastrously harmful.

It is sometimes helpful to discuss drugs in terms
of the undesirability of taking poisons into our
bodies. On the other hand, you can discuss how
your youngsters can achieve healthy, confident and
rewarding living. There are many other approaches
which will occur to you. Give reasons for your
anti-drug stand by exploring the harmful effects of
cannabis, alcohol and other drugs on growing,
developing youngsters. Demonstrate how drugs
lead to dependance instead of self-assured independence. Develop the point that drugs are for sick
people.

The most powerful means of preventing your
youngsters from getting involved in drug abuse is
through ongoing open, caring and honest communication. Through having a good, open, honest
and caring relationship. If you notice the relationship deteriorating, take steps to re-establish it.
Above all, treat your youngster as a person, not
simply as "my child". Take a genuine interest in
his affairs, and particularly his difficulties and
worries in a free, open-ended dialogue. Be sure that
your youngster's feelings are respected and that he
is free to express them. Discounting, or not taking
a youngster's feelings seriously is a sure way of
shutting him off. Don't feel that you have to ask a
string of probing questions. Simply be a good,
relaxed listener, and give adequate time to actively
listening to him. This way you are encouraging the

young person to talk about himself, his interests, and, of course, his worries and fears by making it clear that you are interested.

As early as possible in the youngster's life, *facilitate* him in solving problems for himself. Don't solve problems for him or you rob him of learning experiences and the self-assurance and feeling of competence that comes with the capacity to face and solve problems. Some parents feel obliged to be helpful, to solve their youngster's problems perhaps in order to justify themselves, maybe unwittingly seeing themselves as only of value when they are of help. This may be the parent's problem, and if worked out on the child it could debilitate him and make him or her dependant. If the child is facilitated in problem solving he is likely to develop a strong feeling of competence which will help him in later life, and particularly during adolescence. It has been estimated that parents who apply this approach only spend about 10 per cent of their time with their children, but they tend to have good contact with the youngsters and to be well aware of what is happening with them.

Helping children to solve problems instead of solving them for them obviously involves clearly expressed belief in their ability, and trust in their good sense. This is, of course, not pushed to the point that the youngster is expected to be his own parent. He does need adult guidance. It is an encouraging approach that teaches the youngster also to be self-supporting and self-nourishing, and able to take on increasing levels of responsibility.

I don't think that anything can be more important than openly expressed affection. A great many parental imperfections can be outweighed by the re-assurance, the feeling of being valued for oneself which comes with clearly expressed love and affection. It's not enough to think it, you must say it and express it physically. A hug makes an enormous difference.

On the other hand, nothing can be quite as damaging and devaluing, as bullying or continuous nagging criticism, and particularly, comparing your child to other youngsters. The broad guidelines given above leave plenty of room for inevitable disagreements, outbursts of anger, being irrational and temporarily unfair. You are not perfect. You are a fallible human being whose performance is often erratic and even unreasonable. Attempts at being perfect parents end up in the emasculation of the parent concerned, and produce a caricature of a real, wholesome person. Your anger is also likely to come out sideways, resentments tend to accumulate and erupt in ways that are likely to make you feel ashamed.

A strong, warm-hearted, fallible and fair approach to youngsters is more likely to lead to mutual affection and trust. A youngster's strengths are developed in the home. It is his greatest resource.

What of discipline? Often parents wrongly fear losing the affection of their teenagers if they insist on rules, and having them honoured. A family is a small community of people and each should be expected to do his part in looking after its well-being. Children should have duties and responsibilities in the home ranging from putting the dustbin out to washing up the dishes and they should not be subject to sexual demarcations. Boys can cook too. Doing things together, and participating in the work of the home is a great cementer of relationships, quarrels included.

You have a right to impose reasonable rules in the home in the individual's interest, in your own interest, and that of your other children. The guideline is that the rules be reasonable. Permissiveness is damaging, often a "cop out", and is far more destructive than being a little too strict on occasion. Youngsters do not respect permissiveness. If you look closely at permissiveness you can often recognise the lack of real contact between the permissive parent and the youngster. Sometimes permissiveness is linked to "buying off" a youngster. There is nothing worthwhile that I can think of in the permissive attitude. One further point about it is that without discipline and clear behaviour boundaries, the youngster is left puzzled and uncertain and possibly becomes anxious, self-indulgent, unable to handle frustration. Perhaps the simplest guide is to be honest, be direct, be firm and fair, and let him know your feelings towards him.

Example, of course, is a very powerful influence on youngsters and probably the most damaging example of all is the excessive use of alcohol. This factor emerges again and again in the lives of addicted young people. Excessive alcohol consumption seems to be a dominant factor in the homes of many young addicts. Alcohol and, of course, other drugs deserve to be treated with respect in the home. Nor is it wise to use pills for every minor discomfort or ailment.

Of critical importance is a knowledge of drug related behaviour if you are to be alert for signs of experimenting or early drug abuse. With this knowledge, you are in a position to detect warning signals and take early remedial action. This will be dealt with in Chapter 5, Grounds for Alarm.

The foregoing are factors which should work to protect the youngsters from the influence of the drug environment, and those of his peers who are using drugs. However, just as many drug abusers come from poor homes, many others come from those of more affluent parents. Neglected, or over-indulged, or overpressured youngsters may become dependant on drugs but unfortunately so may youngsters from good, well balanced homes. There is no absolute guarantee that the most enlightened upbringing will protect a youngster from taking, and becoming dependant on drugs.

What we can say is that effective, strong parenting reduces the risks and encourages self-reliance and standards of behaviour. Nevertheless, youngsters do make decisions for themselves. They can make wrong choices through being naive, because of peer pressure, wrong information, erroneous or irrational evaluations, or simply to be perverse, to spite an overambitious parent. The decision to experiment or use drugs can be a combination of factors, particularly pressure from his friends. There are outcomes or consequences resulting from these choices. A youngster may need to be reminded of that fact. However, if you are alert and take quick effective action, it is likely that you can get a youngster back to healthy living again. Consequently you need to be aware of what is happening in his life and be sensitive to changes of behaviour and outlook. Listening, receptive listening, and attention keep that channel open.

Peer Pressure vs. The Home
The pressure from a youngster's peers, that is his friends and acquaintances, can be a very powerful influence on the adolescent and he begins to experience it around the age of 10. Add to this the fact that youngsters are now growing up in a drug environment as a result of which they will be exposed to drugs and intensifying pressure to experiment and use them. Too few parents realise how powerful and persuasive these influential forces are. Nevertheless, parents can succeed in countering these forces, but not without effort. It certainly requires consistent effort and availability.

To understand the pull the youngster experiences to identify with his peers, just look at the clothes your adolescents wear, the phrases they use, the fads, the places they go. They dress and speak this way because it is the current thing to do, and because their friends are doing it. Many of the youngsters try drugs for similar reasons. It is the current thing to do. Happily, most of them will not go any further. Unfortunately, we don't know which ones will continue using drugs and which will subsequently ignore them and get on with their lives.

Adolescence is a confusing and painful period but it is also the most crucial transition phase in the cycle of personal development. Parents have a responsibility to see that they have a healthy environment for their young people, one in which drugs do not intensify and distort, or blot out the normal problems of adolescence. I am referring to the environment in the home, parish and school or wherever the youngster spends his time. Writing on the importance of peer groups Rosenthal and Mothner, 1972 said —

> Adolescents can't tell everything to their parents. They need secrets, they need distance, and they need a wider audience to try their ideas and attitudes on. In some ways, the peer group is in competition with the family, but the adolescent needs both. However, there are dangers in the peer-group situation. Adolescents are very vulnerable to camaraderie, and the values of the group tend to be infectious. If the group's way of dealing with anger at their parents is to steal cars or to use drugs, it is difficult for an individual youngster to resist going along.

It is almost certain that the number of his peers who use drugs is the major influence on a youngster's decision to use them. Consequently, if your youngster's friends are using drugs he is in grave risk. Furthermore, peer loyalty can induce a young person to perform serious misdemeanours. It can also cause some of the rebelliousness and problems in the home. A further quote from Rosenthal and Mothner is relevant here:—

> Your child should have no choice to make about using drugs. You make that choice for him. If you allow him to do anything he wants while you are supporting him, giving him permission to ignore everything you supposedly believe in, you assume an attitude of no attitude, a position of no position. And your child ends up with no position too, because he has no one to challenge, no way he can firm up what he believes.

It can reasonably be said that in recent times there has been an obvious weakening in parental authority and hesitancy about firmness with perhaps more emphasis on being "pals" to their children or in being passive listeners. Elsewhere, in this work, listening is emphasised but it is the active variety. Many parents also seem to have lost conviction about their function and their authority.

It is now generally recognised that this uncertainty can be confusing to children even in close families. They feel much more comfortable and secure when they know the standards expected and the limits allowed.

Religious conviction can be a great bulwark

against drugs, or could be, but there is a great deal of uncertainty about the place of religion in our lives, perhaps a reaction to former excess in creating unnecessary guilt. If religion and related ethical positions are important to parents, they should not delegate the burden of imparting them to the schools. If they are important to parents they should take time to explain them well and make them clear to their children. Religion can be a strong protective counterforce but only if it is understood and is meaningful.

In short, good example may not be sufficient. Youngsters need parents who clearly state standards and values, not as tyrannical injunctions but as important considerations that are valuable and make sense in the youngster's life.

A child development expert, Uric Bronfenbenner has this to say about even the most turbulent families:—

> The relationships in families are the juices of life, the longings and frustrations and intense loyalties. We get our strength from these relationships, we enjoy them, even the painful ones. Of course, we also get some of our problems from them, but the power to survive those problems comes from the family too.

To sum up, the family is the youngster's main bulwark against the influence of the drug culture and peer pressure. Parents can combat drugs. If they don't who else will? In Chapter 7 the effectiveness of parents acting in co-operation with each other to combat the drug environment at neighbourhood, parish, or school level is discussed.

Chapter 4
Communicate with your youngster

Parenting

For most of us the single greatest source of satisfaction or dissatisfaction in life is found in our relationships with others. Unfortunately, our method of communicating often defeats us in our attempts to establish relationships of trust, respect, love, concern, understanding and openness. Often, too, we sacrifice our humanness and individuality by striving to eliminate conflict from our relationships, and as a result eliminate the expression of real feelings.

However, in all interpersonal situations your behaviour communicates something whether or not you intend to. You constantly communicate nonverbally, i.e. by the expression on your face, your body posture, your movements; even your silence is saying something to the other person. Frequently, we give subtle nonverbal cues, or obvious ones like banging a door, to describe our feelings rather than openly admit how we feel. Unfortunately, even though your nonverbal behaviour expresses feelings, it is open to a wide variety of interpretations and is fertile ground for misunderstandings.

When we communicate with someone, be it husband, child or stranger, we are telling them something, sharing or revealing something, particularly what we think, feel and want. We are always communicating and we learned the skill in the course of growing up. In addition, our communication can be either effective or ineffective, leading to increased understanding and a closer relationship or to misunderstanding and distance.

Problems arise mostly in the process of communicating and not as much in personality conflicts as we sometimes think. Our messages get lost, or are misunderstood, because of the ineffective way we send them. Similarly, the quality of our listening will decide how effectively we receive messages. More of this later.

Your child

Communication takes place between people, and you are a person first, and then a parent. Similarly, your child is a person, and not simply an extension of you. Being a human being, you are sometimes inconsistent. On the day that you are feeling well, energetic and in a good mood, your child's behaviour will not give you any trouble. On another day, tired, worried, pressured, you are likely to find the same behaviour a problem. So, you can see that what is acceptable and unacceptable behaviour changes from day to day. Are you being unreasonable, inconsistent, and not living up to your obligations? Not at all, you are simply being human. The variables are usually your mood, and the circumstances — a child running in the garden is quite a different matter to running in the house.

So when your children experience you sometimes tired and at other times relaxed they are learning about variations in other people as well. They don't live in a perfect world and consequently it is realistic for them to see you as less than perfect too. Despite your best efforts at seeming perfect these clear childish eyes see you as you are. Learning that you make mistakes sometimes, that you are a fallible human being, is valuable to them and may also help them avoid the pitfall of making perfectionistic demands on themselves, and the world. We are social beings and getting along with each other requires acceptance of the fact that at times people want to be left alone, or in peace and quiet. Similarly, they learn that parents don't always have time or the energy to play with them. To teach them the facts of social living, you must be a person.

Who owns the problem?
Frequently, parents fall into the trap of taking on the responsibility for their children's problems. They make the problems their own, and try to solve them, rather than helping the child to solve them. To do that, you have to differentiate behaviour which is a problem to you, and behaviour which is saying that the child has a problem. For example, you are trying to talk to another adult, and the child is busy making a racket somewhere. The conversation is important, and the racket is a problem to you, and so you have to do something

about the racket. But — if the child is upset about something, unhappy at school, not getting attention, etc., then he will behave in a way which will tell you something is wrong, that HE has a problem.

Parents sometimes blame themselves, or feel useless or anxious when they can't solve their children's problems. There is now an approach which offers the parents an alternative in helping their children solve their own problems. It is called Parent Effectiveness Training (PET) and it offers a very valuable means for parents to relate to their children in a constructive and mutually enhancing way.

This approach has these basic elements:

(1) All children inevitably will encounter problems in their lives — all shapes and kinds.

(2) All kids have unbelievable and mostly untapped potential for finding good solutions to their problems (watch a baby trying to reach something he wants!)

(3) If parents hand them prepackaged solutions, children remain dependent and fail to develop their own problem-solving skills. They will keep coming to their parents every time they encounter a new problem.

(4) When parents take over (or "own") their childrens' problems, and therefore assume full responsibility for coming up with good solutions, it becomes not only a terrible burden but an *impossible task*. No one has the infinite

wisdom always to generate good solutions for other people's personal problems.

(5)   When a parent can accept that he or she does not own the child's problem he then is in a much better position to be a "helping agent" and help the child work through the problem-solving process on his own.

(6)   Children do need help with certain kinds of problems, but in the long run the kind of help that is most effective, is paradoxically, a form of "non-help". More accurately, it's a new way of helping to leave the responsibility with the child for searching and finding his own solutions. We call these "helping skills".

Listening
"I didn't know what to say". How often do we frantically search for something to *say* when a child comes in with a problem.

What do we say?

Example — 14 year old
"I just can't get down to doing my homework. I hate it. And I hate school".
"I'm going to leave as soon as I can".

Customary responses

| "Indeed you won't — I won't allow it." | – ORDERING, DEMANDING. |
| "O.K., leave, but don't come asking me for help." | – WARNING, THREATENING. |

"Learning is the most rewarding experience anyone can have." — MORALISING, PREACHING

"Why don't you plan out your homework?" — ADVISING, GIVING SOLUTIONS. JUDGING, BLAMING, CRITICIZING, PRAISING, BUTTERING UP, NAME CALLING, RIDICULING. INTERPRETING, ANALYZING, REASSURING, SYMPATHIZING. PROBING, QUESTIONING, INTERROGATING. WITHDRAWING, DIVERTING, DISTRACTING.

The child shuts up, blocked by your ordering etc., and you don't reach the real problem that is bothering him. In this situation you came in too soon, and your ordering, warning, moralising and advising blocked real communication.

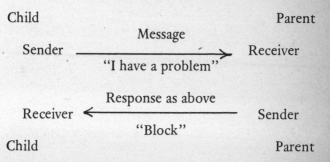

However helpful, practical, or well meant, these responses are frequently blocks to any further communication. They can make youngsters:

stop talking;
go on the defensive;
argue, counter-attack;
feel inadequate, inferior;
feel resentful, angry;
feel guilty or bad;
feel unaccepted as they are;
feel not trusted to solve their own problem;
feel that they are not understood;
feel others' feelings are not justified;
feel interrupted, or cut off;
feel frustrated;
feel cross examined;
feel parents are not interested.

An important principle in human relations is that when someone is in trouble inside, it's seldom helpful to probe, moralise, teach or reassure at that moment. More often than not, being "helpful" in this way stifles problem solving.

This is not to say that you should never be helpful. Sometimes it may be appropriate but mostly it is not. It is better to wait and simply be with the person, being available.

Questions
Asking questions can often be threatening to a youngster and shut off further communication.

For example:
    Child: "I'm not hungry tonight. I just don't feel like eating."
    Parent: "What did you eat after school?"

Child: "Nothing much. That's got nothing to do with it!" (Silence)

There is rather a mean method in use here. The parent has concealed a statement (You were eating sweets) in the form of a question: "What did you eat after school". Assumptions we make about the other person are often expressed in the form of questions. It is not helpful or productive.

"Ask people questions when they have a problem and you will get an answer, but nothing more."

Giving information
This can cut off communication if it is given at the wrong time.

Youngsters are usually not ready to assimilate facts and information, or logic, if they are in an emotional state and their need is to ventilate their feelings. By coming in with information, you discount their feelings and cut them off.

Listen!
Very often, you don't need to give information, advice or solutions. If you know how to listen, and help the child to see what the real problem is, he can more likely find his own solutions. If not, then he will *ask* for information. By quickly coming in with information you diminish the youngster. He will only really learn from experience, his own experience.

Passive Listening (Silence)
The child can't talk if you are doing most of the talking. Your silent attention can convey to someone that you are listening, and interested. You give him plenty of time to talk; your attitude says:

"I want to hear you."

"I accept your feelings."

"I trust you to decide what you want to share with me."

"You are in charge here; it is your problem."

Though useful and necessary, silence is usually not enough. A response is also needed.

Acknowledgement Responses
Child needs to know that it's o.k. to go on; and that you have not gone to sleep. These can range from "Uh, huh!", "Yes", "I see", etc., while looking at him, nodding your head, etc.

Door Openers or Invitations
Sometimes children need encouragement to talk about feelings and problems, especially to get started.

Some ways: "Would you like to talk about it?"

"I'm interested in what you think."

"Sounds like (there is a lot you could say) (you feel very strongly) about that."

"Have you more you could add?"

These are open-ended. They do not ask the child to talk about a specific area — only *what* is going on. Also, there is no evaluation or judgement of what has already been said. Open-ended questions tend to start with "What", "How", seldom "Why" or "Is". Example: (Closed) "Is there anything to do in Waterford?" Reply: "Yes". (Open-ended) "What is there to do in Waterford?" "Well there's . . ."

Active Listening

This is the most effective skill by far. Active listening contains no message from the listener but simply feeds back the child's message. By doing this, the listening parent shows he knows what is being said, and allows the real problems to emerge.
e.g. The same 14 year old.

> "(I hate school). I can't get down to doing homework. I'm going to leave as soon as I can."

A.L. Response:

> "You are finding it hard to get the homework done."
> "Yes, it is really getting to me. I am sick of it. We are getting more and more all the time, and I do not know where to begin."
> "You are a bit lost with it all, the more you get to do, the worse you feel." etc., etc.

This response is more likely to keep the child talking for a while about how worried he is. Then he has a better chance to find a practical solution, once the feelings have been ventilated and he has had an ear to listen.

Attitudes required to use Active Listening
To be an effective listener, there are certain attitudes that must be present.

1. You must *want* to hear what the child has to say. This means you are willing to take time to listen. If you don't have time, you need only say so.

2. You must genuinely want to be helpful to him with his particular problem at that time. If you don't want to, wait until you do.

3. You must genuinely be able to *accept his feelings*, whatever they may be or however different they may be from your own feelings or from the feelings you think a child "should" have.

4. You must have a deep feeling of *trust* in the child's capacity to handle his feelings, to work through them, and to find solutions to his problems. You will acquire this trust by watching your child solve his own problems.

5. You must appreciate that feelings are *transitory*, not permanent. Feelings change — hate can turn into love, discouragement may quickly be replaced by hope. Consequently, you need not be afraid of feelings getting expressed; they will not become forever fixed inside the child. Active listening will demonstrate this to you.

6. You must be able to see your child as *someone separate* from you — a unique person no longer joined to you, a separate individual having been given by you his own life and his own identity. This separateness will enable you to permit the child to have his own feelings, his own way of perceiving things. Only by feeling separateness will you be able to be a helping agent for the child. You are with him as he experiences his problems, but not joined to him.

There is a risk. Your own thoughts and feelings have to be suspended temporarily to listen to the message. When you put yourself in somebody's shoes you risk *changing*. Rigid and defensive people find it hard to change. Youngsters who have parents who are willing to change, can meet change better themselves. This approach to parenting is called parent effectiveness training, developed by Dr. Thomas Gordon. *P.E.T. in Action*, Bantam Books, is an excellent, clear guide for parents, which I thoroughly recommend.

Common Erroneous child-rearing beliefs
Three of the more common yet erroneous beliefs about child-rearing that are particularly destructive to children are discussed here: children must not disagree with their parents; children must not be frustrated; children should be calmed first, adults second. Also outlined are the patterns of child-rearing grounded in combinations of these patterns.

The ideas given here are a synopsis of those of

Dr. Paul A. Hanck, a leading figure in the treatment of disturbed children, and parents and families, using the [1] Rational Emotive Therapy (RET) approach.

It is useful to ask yourself some questions regarding objectionable behaviour in children. Is this behaviour a manipulation to attain the goal of attention, power, revenge or disability? For example, he could be depressed for attention, angry to prove that he is more powerful than you, fearful to revenge himself against a worried you, or poorly self-disciplined to prove he is weak and afraid of growing up so that no adult demands will be made of him. Or is the behaviour — fear, anger, depression, poor self-discipline a neurotic symptom of irrational thinking?

All of these behaviours stem from common parenting errors. A common error is not allowing children to think for themselves, and to learn through hard experience.

As youngsters enter their teens, overnight a nice boy or girl may become mean and disobedient, and a power struggle begins with the questioning of everything he/she has ever been told. Back off, you can let them question and shape their lives according to what they find out the hard way. Out of the testing of their ideas comes greater self-confidence, and what they learn from their mistakes.

[1] Handbook of Rational Emotive Therapy; Ellis & Grieger, Springer Publishing Co. Inc. Published by Sheldon Press. "Be Calm" and other excellent works by Dr. Hanck can be obtained through Irish bookshops.

Frustration Phobia—children must not be frustrated
Often parents try in every way to make life so easy and pleasant for their youngsters that frustration has ·become a dirty word. Unfortunately, protecting them in this way is harmful. The value of living through frustration and growing strong in the process is not sufficiently appreciated. Parents want so much to spare their children pain that the youngsters often don't know how to tolerate it — and carry on working effectively at the same time. Consequently, a youngster may erroneously believe that he should not be expected to do his work when he is unhappy. If this is so, he will not learn to put up with and handle the unpleasantness in life. To this kind of person, alcohol and other drugs are an attractive option. For example, parents often cannot bear to let a youngster go without pocketmoney if he has unwisely spent all his allowance within days of receiving it. Inability to bear frustration is a major characteristic of the neurotic, the immature, and the drug addict. Learning to endure frustration and stress is an important part of becoming strong. Self-discipline and the demands it makes for delayed satisfaction is one of the greatest benefits to be gained through temporary distress. If we endure some pain now, we endure less pain eventually.

Who's angry?
Many parents erroneously believe that a youngster should be the first to calm down, and after that the parent. A youngster gives some backtalk and the

parent gets angry. In effect, you ask the youngster to control himself in a mature way, but you, the supposedly mature adult, can get as angry as you like. You insist that he get a hold of himself, then you will get hold of yourself. Parents should learn to calm themselves first and then deal fairly with the disturbing behaviour of their child. It will also lessen the amount of neurotic blaming that you do. Blaming is a most damaging activity and results in feelings of inferiority and depression.

Be Firm — without being mean
If you have a complaint to make to your youngster, say it in a relatively matter-of-fact way, and not with great feeling. Unfortunately, discipline in child-rearing is flavoured with doses of unkindness. Here is an example: Mother: "Don't come to the dinner table until you have washed your hands". This is a reasonable request and sets a standard. Often, however, a mean follow-up goes like this: "Why do you always have to be difficult? Do you always have to give me so much trouble?" This could ultimately lead to guilt, depression and resentment. Daily put-downs, blaming criticisms, are insidious and destructive, and can produce scared, nervous, insecure and inferior-feeling children. Also, if you are continually angry it is almost impossible to convince a youngster that you love him. I would add, drop the word "stupid" from your vocabulary when speaking to a youngster.

But, as the following pages show, kindness on its own is not enough.

Kind but not firm

Instead of raising scared, nervous, insecure, and inferior-feeling children, parents who are kind but not firm raise youngsters who, being seldom frustrated, set up their own rules, often get their way and tend to be spoiled brats. They are usually whiners, the darlings who get threatened if you turn your back to talk to someone, and they act like eternal babies. Even if they do emerge as relatively pleasing people they still live under great fear of having to live on their own someday.

A youngster's strength of character doesn't come from your being too helpful. Letting a youngster suffer a little, allowing him to work his own way out of pain will enable him to develop into a real adult. Denied this opportunity, his life may forever be lonely, unfulfilled, and largely unhappy. And what will he go through when his parents die?

In marriage if these people can't have what they want the result is misery. At all ages they react to each disappointment as though they were five years old and were denied an ice cream. They need to learn the ability to put up with frustration. Helping too much isn't helping them!

Unkind but not firm

How can a child win if he is yelled at, scolded, told he's no good, but at the same time, has no strong hand over him making him correct his irritating behaviour?

It is one thing to yell at an adolescent for not studying and then ground him or penalise him until he brings his marks up, and it is entirely another thing for him to be screamed at for poor marks and then allowed to stay out every night after dark. He lacks control. He is expected to be his own conscience and supervisor, his own parent, with the wisdom to do what is right even though he is only a child.

Take the mother who yells at the truant child, but doesn't sit on him hard enough to bring him back into line. All she does is complain more and more and do less and less.

Often parents are afraid to face an angry child, or face the rejection of a child they feel like disciplining. They can't stand the temporary dislike of their own children. You can conclude that what children don't learn at home they learn the hard way, some on drugs or in jail.

Kind but firm

It is important to be decent, understanding, patient with children, *but* it is equally important to expect, unangrily and unblamingly, that children face life and its frustration squarely. Love is not enough and, as often conceived, can be ruinous to the character development of a child.

It matters little if a young thief has a wicked stepmother and an alcoholic father. What matters is that he understands that HE has a problem or he's going to spend a lot of time in jail unless he stops stealing. We don't have to hate him; we don't blame him for being under the sway of antecedent conditioning. He may be. All that is really irrelevant. What he will want to develop (if he wants to stay out of jail, psychiatric hospital, or clinic) is to accept responsibility for his *current* behaviour and work hard to change it.

Chapter 5
Grounds for Alarm

Despite your most concerned efforts as a parent, you may become puzzled, anxious or even alarmed at your youngster's behaviour and perhaps suspect drug abuse. As I indicated earlier, it often takes up to three years for parents to become really aware that something is seriously wrong. Why so long? Well, in the early stage, young people involved with drugs are sometimes still able to exercise some self-control so that they do not give themselves away at home. They take elaborate precautions to deceive their parents. However, in the long run moods. behaviour and other indicators signal that all is not well.

Also, most parents are not knowledgeable about drug abuse and the changes in the person that go with it. They may dismiss odd behaviour as typically adolescent. Often it is, but because of the drug environment which exists today and the pressures to use drugs, it is best to be alert to the possibility of involvement with drugs. Ignorance of this area is no longer really acceptable since the danger is now known and it is growing in intensity.

It is surprising how many parents reject out of hand the possibility that their children are using drugs, or dismiss experimenting as "no harm", and to be expected. Even more puzzling is the hostile reaction of some parents when they are given accurate information about their children's drug use. Teachers, in particular, are acutely aware of these possible reactions and are understandably loath to incur parental wrath by alerting them. This places a severe limit on the possibility of early warning and early preventive action. Parents have been known to change schools because of an alert received from a teacher. It is particularly unfortunate since teachers are in an excellent position to notice changes in the youngster, particularly a drop in school performance.

Parents are familiar with the normal adolescent's urge to experiment and seek new experiences, to reject and rebel, and to reach out to people outside the home. However, when drugs enter the scene this healthy urge can lead him into the drug culture through knocking around with drug abusers. He needs alert, interested parents who can take early action to protect him.

Parents are still the youngster's best defence against the pressures of the drug culture and they need to realise that at this important stage in their lives youngsters are very credulous. They are eager and receptive to new ideas, and myths, particularly if they are at variance to the expectations, opinions, and beliefs of parents, teachers and other authority figures.

It is essential that parents give more time to adolescents, to listening to them and being sensitive and alert to what is happening to them.

This may not always be welcomed, particularly during their withdrawn and secretive phases but in fact it does reassure the adolescent that you are interested and concerned. Discussing their interests and concerns with them keeps you close to them and places you in a position to broach many questions in an open, conversational way.

What should you be on the lookout for?
Well, alcohol is easy to detect because of its odour. You will probably not be able to detect signs of cannabis, other hallucinogens or tablets, initially. Youngsters often disguise the use of cannabis by smoking cigarettes or drinking beer, or by using incense, perfume or deodorants in their room. There is no way of being absolutely sure except by finding the drugs themselves, or drug paraphernalia. Some parents ask about tablets they have found and wonder if they are dangerous. The real issue is why their youngster has tablets at all.

If you know your youngster, you are certainly likely to notice changes in his behaviour or appearance. Ask yourself these questions:

Has his schoolwork deteriorated?
Is he keeping odd hours?
Has he lost weight?
Has his appearance deteriorated, changing from sloppy to downright dirty?
Have his capabilities dropped in work habits, study, efficiency, etc.?
If he has been keen on sport and other involv-

ing activities, has he dropped them?
Is he frequently vague or withdrawn?

Nothing of absolute certainty here, since many of these changes may be typical of adolescents at one time or another, or of difficult adolescence. Their need for privacy may also make them secretive. However, they are not to be overlooked in today's climate and if you know your child and recognise a combination of these changes, you have good grounds for examining his behaviour more closely.

Look out for:

> Poor control over his impulses.
> Has his thinking become muddled, confused?
> Can't tolerate frustration and must get immediate satisfaction.
> Depression. Starting to sleep a lot.
> Are there times when he seems overactive, or excessively talkative?
> Doesn't participate actively any more.
> Scratching himself frequently (Opiates).
> Continuous sniffles, red, watering eyes and cough.

THESE ARE DANGER SIGNALS

Excessive complaining may indicate that because of drug use he is unable to cope with normal adolescent stress.

A combination of naivete, unwillingness to intrude on the adolescent, bafflement, and a lack

INDICATION OF DANGER

If you observe these symptoms	Or these drug-related items
Running nose, no appetite, drowsiness, stupor, watering eyes, irritable, yawning, bloodstained sleeves, needle marks on arms, etc.	Syringe, needles, cotton wool, belt for tourniquet; burnt spoons, bottle caps.
Disorientation, drunken behaviour, slurred speech, also with smell of alcohol.	Tablets, bottles.
Agitation, confusion, dry mouth, shaking, aggressiveness, silly giggling, loss of appetite, rapid speech, apathy, depression, irritability, long sleeps.	Powder, tablets of various kinds.
Incoherent speech, hallucinations, laughing.	Sugar cubes, spots on paper, strong body smell, tubes of liquid.
Enlarged pupils, craves sweets, increased appetite, no co-ordination or concentration, sleepiness, wears dark glasses indoors.	Sweet odour of burnt rope, seeds, cigarette paper, burnt tweezers, dried leaves, crudely rolled cigarettes, similar cigarette ends, pieces of cardboard.
Blank or dreamy expression, may appear drunk or be violent, hallucinating.	Tubes of glue, glue smears, large plastic or paper bags, handkerchiefs.
Itching, confusion, no co-ordination, seems drunk.	Cough bottles.

See Chapter 12 for detailed description of drugs.

Drugs suspected	Risks of drugs
Heroin Diconal Opium Palfium Morphine Methedone Codeine Pethedine	Fatal dose possibility. Hepatitis — liver damage or failure, Convulsions, death.
Barbiturates Alcohol Antihistamines Sedatives Tranquillisers Sleeping tablets	Fatal overdose possibility with alcohol. Withdrawal: convulsions, possible death.
Cocaine Amphetamines Ritalin Weight reducing drugs	Heart Strain, Overdose, hallucinations, convulsions, death.
LSD Mescalin Peyote	Brain damage from chronic use; unpredictable behaviour; in some cases possible suicide. Psychosis.
Marijuana/ Cannabis Hashish Hashish Oil	Paranoia, fatigue, possible psychosis, drop-out. Possible damage to lungs, reproductive system. Dependence.
Inhalants; glues, petrol, cleaning fluids and aerosols.	Choking — brain, lung or liver damage. Anaemia, death.
Cough mixture with codeine or opium.	Addictive.

of knowledge about drugs and drug-related behaviour frequently prevent parents from observing warning signals. Now let's move to other indicators:

Has he become suspicious, reserved, unfriendly?

Does he wear sunglasses indoors or when there is obviously no sunshine? Sunglasses are often used to hide dilated or constricted pupils due to drug use, and to compensate for the eye's inability to adjust to sunlight, or to conceal bloodshot eyes resulting from smoking cannabis.

Does he associate with known drug abusers? (This is of major significance).

Does he make unusual efforts to cover his arms (to hide needle marks)?

Are items which can be easily sold vanishing from the house?

Have cheques been removed from a cheque book?

Has he suddenly started eating a lot of sweets?

Started spending a lot of time in the toilet? (Possibly injecting).

If you observe any of these indications, start spending much more time with your youngster. Find out more about his activities and get to know more about his friends. Be alert to other developments, like strange youngsters and older people calling to the house asking for him. Don't erupt and accuse him of using drugs. Calmly and non-judgementally ask him if he is drinking, smoking pot or using other drugs.

If he denies using drugs, but the symptoms continue, you had better intensify your investigations of his friends, his environment and his activities. You now have sufficient grounds for taking measures that you would not otherwise contemplate. You have a right, and an obligation, to make more detailed enquiries, and to search his room and belongings. There is nothing sneaky or underhand about such measures. You are his guardian, guide and mentor and in his best interest you must protect him. If you don't take these steps, you are failing him when he needs your active concern most. Furthermore, you have the right to protect your home from drugs and the illegal activities that go with them. Your other children also depend on your protection and vigilance.

It is possible that you may find physical signs, e.g. a butt from a cannabis joint. Cannabis joints are like loosely filled cigarettes since they are hand rolled. You may detect the sweet odour, like burnt rope, of cannabis. You may discover burnt pieces of cardboard, seeds, leaves, rolling paper for cigarettes, match boxes, lots of used matches, burnt spoons, alcohol containers, metal bottle caps, cotton, powders, pills, eyedrop bottles, incense, room deodorisers. Puncture marks, probably on his arm. Obvious items include syringes, needles, tablets, medical prescriptions, burnt sheets resulting from the youngster falling asleep, or blood on shirts.

You should now take immediate action. Don't approach the subject when he is "stoned" or drunk, or while you are still angry. Don't get into sophisticated arguments on the relative dangers of alcohol, cannabis or other drugs. Your approach must be no drugs, including alcohol, in the home, or while he is living at home. When youngsters, and others, speak of cannabis as being safer than alcohol (or that it should be legalised) remember that the reality is that the youngster will almost certainly use both alcohol and cannabis. If you don't take effective measures at this stage you could be allowing him to slide further into addiction. Later, he will not hesitate to blame you when his life has gone seriously wrong.

Your approach to the situation should be firm, honest and respectful of the youngster as a person. It is wrong and unproductive to treat him as if he were a criminal or to make him feel that he is rejected. Make it clear that it is the drugs, the drug-related behaviour and the lying involved, that you reject, and that your concern is for his growth and well being. The fact that he is behaving badly does not justify draconian measures or bullying put-downs.

Chapter 6
Take a Stand!

When parents are convinced that a youngster is experimenting or using drugs, the time has arrived to take immediate and sustained action. Parents understandably feel shocked, humiliated and ashamed that a son or daughter is involved with drugs. The danger is that they may become overwhelmed with guilt and accept too much responsibility for what has happened, forgetting that youngsters have minds of their own. The inevitable question, "What did I do wrong?", can lead into an emotional dead-end. Youngsters are not blank pages on which parents write in the correct behaviour, attitudes, morals and values. Young people can misinterpret their experiences and their relationships with their parents, and reach irrational and self-defeating conclusions about life. Excessive guilt on the part of parents can immobilise them and divert them from taking the steps which must be taken. In addition, feeling guilty and ashamed, parents often spend their energies in covering up for the youngsters, making up stories to mislead the neighbours, and relatives.

Parents are under no obligation to tell others about the drug problem in their home. Energies put into covering up, however, can be better employed in problem solving with the youngster. Furthermore, knowing that parents are covering up can give the more manipulative and aggressive youngsters power over their parents.

One further point about the reaction of parents. Some react angrily and proceed to impose a punitive regime on the youngster. Ventilating anger may bring some relief to the heated parent, but that is probably all that will be achieved. The youngster may react with greater sullenness and resistance, if not outright rebelliousness. Angry denunciations do not create relationships. Wait until your anger has passed.

When the first shock is over, take a firm emotional and intellectual stand and make it absolutely clear that you will not allow the young person to use drugs, including alcohol. Be sure in your own mind that this is an issue on which you must not compromise. Mean what you say, and carry it through.

Then commence an ongoing dialogue with your youngster giving plenty of time to him or her. Share your feelings about his drug abuse and let him know just how hurt and upset you feel. Also, share your worries and your fears about his drug use. Stick to the facts about drugs and avoid exaggeration which will only diminish you in his eyes.

In getting together with your son, insist that he participates with you in studying the effects of both legal and illegal drugs. Relate these to the problems experienced by his age group. Discuss the material on drugs in Chapter 12. Try to get him to think about and understand the normal developmental changes of adolescence, the moods, conflicts, physical changes, sexual worries, frustration, and other related matters. Help him to understand that these need to be met and experienced by him, and understood, and accepted. This process of teenage growth must not be avoided, interrupted or blotted out by drugs or alcohol, otherwise he will end his adolescence immature and dependant.

The vital message here is that adolescence is a period of learning, an experience that leads to maturity. By facing and managing pressure, tolerating frustration, coping with depression, boredom, and coming through loneliness, and inevitable pain, a youngster becomes an adult able to cope and rely on his own power and resources. If, however, the young person tries to evade coping with these experiences, by using cannabis, or other drugs, including alcohol, he may end this phase handicapped by an inability to handle frustration or to cope with life's difficulties with assurance. As an American colleague puts it, "He may be a 20 year old going on 14".

Probably the state most prized by adolescents is independence. Your most potent arguments lie in this area. Be honestly clear in your presentation of your thoughts on growth and independence. Share your hopes for, and your confidence in, his eventual independence. Let him know that the rebellious use of drugs while looking like independence is in fact self-defeating and ends in dependance. Be direct and honest in presenting this argument. Describe for him what you mean by a confident, independent person. For example, you can see him as one who is in charge of his impulses and emotions, has a clear and capable mind, a healthy body, with plenty of energy, a cheerful and optimistic attitude, and able to tackle life with a feeling of competence; able to make long term plans and carry them out. None of these natural developments go with drugs. On the contrary, drug use merely leads to dependence and the manipulating of others into doing what he needs to do for himself.

The following is a summary of the reasons you can give for your stand against all drug (alcohol) taking:

• During their adolescence youngsters need to learn to cope with the frustrations, anxieties, depressions and self-doubt of these troubled years and, from the experience, emerge as healthy, independent adults. The only way out of this phase is to go through it. Cannabis, alcohol and other drugs blot out this experience and it is an escape from growing up. Youngsters huddling over a "joint" are in effect opting out, hiding from sexual and other anxiety, loneliness, personal doubts and other problems adolescents must confront in order to become responsible, self-assured grown-ups in charge of their own lives. If they never come to grips with these problems, they will end their teenage years only partially finished adults without the skills, the successful coping experiences, the feeling of competence they need to cope with life. If a youngster wishes to achieve independence and self-assurance, drugs can have no place in his life — one excludes the other.

• By using drugs, their capability to learn and gain experience will be diminished and memory, judgement, co-ordination and motor skills will be affected. School work will deteriorate, well-liked sporting activities will ultimately be abandoned as drugs begin to dominate and take over the life of the youngster.

• Virtually all drug-dependent youngsters started experimenting with the confident belief that they could choose to stop whenever they liked. In the early stages they may even be able to demonstrate this, thereby reinforcing their over-confidence. Unfortunately, their confidence does not control the effects of drugs and the onset of psychological and physiological addiction. Over-confidence can be the Achilles Heel of the teenager. It is pathetic to hear addicted young people still asserting that they can stop whenever they choose, when they are so obviously "hooked". By starting with drugs he has nothing to gain, and everything to lose. Maybe his life.

• Drugs damage the body and the mind. They are unhealthy poisons deliberately introduced into the system.

• Cannabis is not harmless, nor is alcohol, or any of the other drugs. Most heroin addicts started on cannabis and/or alcohol, and progressed to heroin. Marijuana is called the "drop out" drug because users often become apathetic, give up on life and their work or studies, their ambitions, and lose all sense of responsibility.

• Drugs destroy the reality of life. His mind is a youngster's most valuable asset — with it he appreciates the sights and sounds of life as real, not dreamed. The pleasure of living is in experiencing the actual, in sensing and responding to life.

• Psychological dependence is the first step to addiction. Psychological dependence is almost a certainty if youngsters persist in using drugs, and physical addiction is eventually almost equally inevitable, particularly in the case of barbiturates and the opiates, if the youngster does not wake up and leave them alone.

• Drugs are for sick people, and not for growing, maturing youngsters. If they persist with drugs, they do in fact become sick people.

• Involvement with drugs is probably the quickest and most certain way to getting arrested and finding oneself in jail. With it goes the mean, unprincipled and grubby life of the addict obsessed with but one thought — drugs, and how to get the money to pay for them. Getting the price of drugs eventually leads to crime and the consequences of crime — prison sentences.

• Finally, apart from dependence on drugs, there are the risks: cirrhosis of the liver, hepatitis, brain damage, proneness to fatal accidents, overdose and death.

Having talked to your youngster about what you have observed of his moodiness, avoidance, detachment, and other behaviour, try to open the conversation to include what his fears are, what he likes, his preferences, and what he hopes to become. Let him tell you about how he feels. Too many parents discount youngsters' feelings. They are told that they shouldn't feel the way they do. Feelings are a part of the facts about a person's experience. When they seem to get a youngster into trouble, he may try to hide them or suppress them through regarding them as troublesome. Locked in and guarding his feelings, he experiences greater difficulties. Feelings come in order to go and when acknowledged and experienced they go on their way. Don't make it a cross-examination or nag him.

You will need patience and you will do best by doing a lot of listening. Don't jump in with solutions and suggestions but wait and let him talk. Be a good listener, better than you have ever been before. Allow the young person to edge closer to you. Your quick, logical solutions and suggestions, though satisfying your need to be helpful, may only create a barrier.

In being warm, patient, and understanding, don't lose sight of the stand you have taken on drugs. On this issue you cannot compromise. All too many parents have been reduced to humbly accepting, "It's not so bad, he's only on cannabis". They have been manipulated and are lying to themselves. They may be pre-occupied with comforting themselves rather than helping to solve their youngster's problem. Don't lower your standards or be manipulated into bargaining and settling for alleged limited use of cannabis or alcohol. You will regret it.

Some parents even become afraid of their teenager or fear the displeasure of their youngster. What the youngster needs now is a strong parent. Being a strong parent does not mean being an unfeeling martinet. Strong is what you need to be at this point.

You may very well be tested, depending on the stage of drug abuse the youngster has reached. If advanced in drugs, he may blame you for his condition, or society, the West, everyone except himself. However, in the early stages you are only likely to experience the normal testing of discipline or permissive boundaries. A strong parent is a good role model and a resource to a youngster at this stage. In addition, strong parents are involved with their youngster in a way that the permissive, lax, selfish, over-strict or distant parents very seldom are.

Follow up your "no drugs" stand with realistic, fair, consistent rules on behaviour and commit yourself to seeing that they are carried out. The rules need to be fair and reasonable leaving room for the person to develop and respect himself. Draconian measures that humiliate, or leave no room for any recreation are unfair and can't be justified. You are leading, disciplining, and guiding the youngster, not conquering or humbling him. After all, your ultimate objective for him is responsible and confident independence.

Taking into account your youngster's needs for recreation and special interests, a parent should set out clearly what is expected of the youngster. For example, spell out your expectations regarding the time to be devoted to the completion of homework, jobs to be done in your home and the time he is expected to return home at night. Your stand should be clear on time devoted to girlfriends, the kind of people you will allow to phone and the respect you want shown to each other in the home in terms of manners, concern and behaviour. The objective is not simply to be restrictive but to get the relationship onto open, honest, clear lines with as few vague areas as possible left open for misunderstanding. If his drug taking is serious, you may have to ground him for a period and see to it that he stays at home after school. You should leave adequate room for recreation at home.

Drugs are circulated within the social circles, and the youngster's network, of friends, and the places they meet and visit. Consequently, these areas must be kept under observation until the problem is overcome and the youngster resumes normal activities, including satisfactory schoolwork.

What do you do about group activities? Parties, for example? This is a nettle that some parents may be reluctant to grasp. However, if drugs are being circulated, these affairs need to be supervised by an informed adult whatever the objections. Currently, alcohol is freely available at parties, and often cannabis even though parents may be sitting in the next room. Where a youngster has been found to be using drugs, permissiveness and/or reluctance to supervise these affairs is a betrayal of responsibility. Certainly, such measures may be unpopular, but unpopularity is a small price to pay if you succeed in protecting your youngster from drifting into addiction. You will need to get the co-operation of other parents to implement this policy.

It would be up to the person delegated to supervise the party or gathering to keep a clear eye on the event so that he or she notices the disappearance of youngsters, or if anyone appears drunk or "stoned". Your own ground rules have a direct bearing on these and other functions. If your youngster knows that there is a strong likelihood of being caught if he breaks the rules, he is likely to resist pressure from his group of friends to use drugs or alcohol.

It cannot be over-emphasised that the purpose at this stage is to restore the youngster to normal life. It is not to impose a punishing regime. If fair rules are broken, reasonable consequences should be applied on each occasion until you convince him that you do mean what you say. No doubt, some parents will object that it is difficult to impose rules on young teenagers. It may be, if your authority has been eroded, but it is not impossible. If imposed in the right spirit, the youngster will eventually recognise the fairness and consistency of the rules. Obviously, the period over which this becomes effective may be weeks or months but you must convince the youngster that you are in earnest and that there are real and immediate consequences for breaches of the rules. Your purposefulness and resolution will be an anchor for your son or daughter to hold on to as he or she returns to normal life and avoids drugs.

If the youngster is likely to be under pressure from his acquaintances to use drugs, then having him stay at home after school for a period may be the most effective means of helping him. It also means that he will be around the home sufficiently long to enable you to talk to him about his fears and problems, his interests and other matters of significance in his life, and yours. It could enable you both to come closer if done in the right spirit. You may also need to forbid the use of the telephone so that undesirable acquaintances are kept at bay. Difficult, perhaps unpleasant, but necessary.

While homebound, it need hardly be said that tablets or liquor should not be accessible. Lock them up. This is the reality of the situation. To ensure that no drugs are secreted in the house you may need to search the house, and his room, periodically. You may be accused with, "you don't trust me". The honest answer is that you don't and can't trust him until he earns your trust once more. He has abused it and he can recover it when he proves trustworthy. Young people who get involved with drugs become very adept in creating guilt in their parents. If in discussion with your youngster you begin to feel guilty, pause and examine what is happening between you. Are you being manipulated and wrong footed? If you are, say so and with it what you feel about being manipulated.

Needless to add, if the person has been consistently using drugs, you will have to wait until his thinking and body are cleared before change can take place. Often, for example, for a youngster who has been using cannabis consistently it will take him up to a month before he returns to his normal self. If he has been using barbiturates it is most unwise to withdraw the drug immediately. Seek help and guidance from the National Drugs Advisory and Treatment Centre, Jervis Street Hospital.

Clearly you will need to give serious thought to grading the consequences you are prepared to impose in relation to the seriousness of the misdemeanours. You can withdraw other privileges like looking at T.V., having a radio or record player. The consequences should match the rule broken.

This may prove a painful or difficult period, but productive if it results in saving your youngster from drugs. Later, much later, he will probably appreciate your concerned action. I know of many instances where this has happened.

The consequences, if you do not act, are likely to be beyond anything that you can imagine. Apart from the ravages of drug addiction and possible overdose and death, the havoc wrought in the home is quite unbelievable.

Once in a while at a Parents Action and Prevention Programme public meeting a parent asks

"Aren't these measures severe?" or "I couldn't impose rules on my youngsters, they'd laugh at me". If youngsters are not involved in drugs or with drug abusing people, these emergency protective measures are not necessary. If they are involved, they need protection. The question is: Is it your uppermost concern to protect your youngster from drugs? And are you willing to take every possible measure to protect him even though it will make you temporarily unpopular with him? Or are you willing to risk his future and perhaps his life rather than insist on firm ground rules in your home? You are up against the effects of drugs on your youngster's personality. Reasoning alone won't help. You have to insist on protective rules. If he had pneumonia you wouldn't let him out. Drugs are infinitely more dangerous and there is no antibiotic for the effect of drugs.

I believe that youngsters have a right to expect their parents to be a rock, or anchor, that they can hang on to when they are in danger of being swept into the drug culture under the pressure of their peers. In this situation, youngsters desperately need resolute parents. They need parents who will be strong for them.

Early action has the greatest chance of success. And even at an early stage, contact the counsellors at the National Drugs Advisory and Treatment Centre, Jervis Street Hospital, Dublin, phone 01-723355, and the Coolemine Family and Friends Association, phone 01-214545. The NDATC will give you excellent advice and guidance based on their long experience. Parents in the Coolemine Family Association will also give you first hand experience, advice, and support. You need all the support and guidance you can get. Nevertheless, resolute action must be taken by *you*. If you seek advice from other quarters, find out their stand on the use of cannabis by juveniles. If they condone it, leave them alone.

Obviously, the younger the age when drug abuse is discovered the easier it is to handle. Youngsters up to the age of 16 years are more easily managed because they are still sufficiently young to be influenced. When youngsters reach the age of 17 and 18 years it is much more difficult to handle them if they are abusing drugs. It is therefore vital to be alert to signs of drug abuse in the early teenage years when your intervention is more likely to lead to success.

Chapter 7
Parents Acting Together

It is almost certain that few neighbourhoods or parishes, in the Dublin area particularly, are free of drugs or some level of alcohol abuse by adolescents. The influence of the intruding drug environment, the pressure, the challenge, to drink and smoke cannabis is now such that youngsters cannot avoid contact with drugs and the drug culture. As long as it is there it will intensify and your youngster and his friends are seriously at risk. And drink and cannabis smoking are the introduction to the mood altering experience, the curtain raisers for the drug culture.

Acting alone you can be effective in protecting your youngster. However, taking a stand can be a lonely experience. Fortunately, there is an alternative to this isolation — co-operation with other parents. You could build a community of families which could shape and exercise a large measure of control over your children's immediate environment. By working together you would be creating a form of extended family subscribing to certain values, and expectations.

There are many ways of approaching this. One, is to bring together the parents of your youngster's friends, a parent peer group. Another, is to form a group of parents in your own parish or neighbourhood. A third way is to form a support group at your school. As a guideline, remember that youngsters begin to experience peer pressure from the age of 10 years.

Such a group would reinforce the stand you are taking at home. The complaints, and protests of your youngster at your stand will be less likely to undermine your determination. In addition, the "everyone is doing it" ploy will not impress you. Adolescents will endeavour to make you feel old-fashioned and try to convince you that you are the only one enforcing rules. Don't fall for it!

Parents acting together can have a great deal of power and it is the only power likely to push back the pressure of your youngster's drug abusing acquaintances and the drug environment. And the truth is that the pressure to use drugs has pervaded all levels of our society with hardly any community opposition. It need not have happened, but the increasing numbers of young casualties is the reminder that it is becoming an ominous threat to our way of life. So insidious has been its influence that otherwise responsible and sensible people still ask, "But isn't cannabis safe?" Standards have been eroded and drugs are becoming more and more acceptable — unless we take action. And only parents can really do it effectively because they have power where it counts most, in the home and in their neighbourhood. Collectively, parents can also use their power to clean drugs out of the neighbourhood and make it safe for their youngsters.

A promising area of co-operative action is with the parents of your youngsters' friends. Or you might favour a neighbourhood group. Get those who are interested to help you organise a meeting. If necessary, do it yourself. *Phone, or call on these parents*. Needless to add, you will have to be diplomatic since some will not want to know. If you already know of cannabis use, or underage drinking, you could open with "A problem may be developing. I understand that some of our youngsters are smoking cannabis and drinking. I think that it would be a good idea if we get together and talk about it".

You can anticipate that a percentage of those you call on will shrug it off or deny that anything is happening. Others may express disbelief and convey the impression that you are a busybody. If you are prepared for some such resistance, it will be less likely to upset or deter you. Probably the best approach is to make it a straight statement of concern about what is happening or likely to happen, and leave it at that. Don't get involved in persuading, defending or pushing the idea. Your message will be much more effective when stated simply. It is then the other parents' responsibility to respond. If there is denial, resistance, don't get involved, simply say something like — "I thought you should know. If you are interested, you will be welcome to come to our meeting."

Hold your first meeting in your home, or that of someone else, or at the school, etc. The first step will be to share whatever information you have, your concern and your belief that collectively you can take effective steps to deal with the situation before it gets beyond control. Some more information will probably be offered by other parents. It is all too easy at this stage to settle on several names of troublesome teenagers and make them the scapegoats. The drug problem is much more complex than that. Certainly, there may be older youths using drugs and supplying them to younger boys and girls and steps will have to be taken to counter their influence. However, at your first meeting stick to gathering information.

Open the meeting with a conciliatory statement like "The purpose of this meeting is not to make accusations about our youngsters. We don't know what is really happening but we have grounds for believing that drugs/drink are circulating or being used, and we feel that we should do something about it."

Arrange to hold a further meeting and use the interval for all to gather further facts about what is happening in the neighbourhood, at the school, or where youngsters gather, and to get further facts about the drug environment in your area. You could consult agencies (listed at the end of this section) dealing with the drug problem for further information and guidance.

Your group will elicit a good deal of co-operation if it goes about its task in a moderate, concerned way. Should the group adopt an aggressive, blaming or challenging approach it is likely to provoke hostility and fail to win co-operation. The objective is a caring neighbourhood. The spirit in which you tackle the problem is of vital importance. Being self-righteous, bullying or witch-hunting, repels others who might otherwise be supporters. Share your knowledge and concern with other parents, business people, community leaders, Dáil Deputies, tenants' associations, in your community. Speak to other parents.

An important aspect of the fact finding will, of course, include speaking to your youngsters. If you are certain that drugs are circulating, emphasise that you would prefer to hear about what is happening from him first, particularly if he is involved, however innocently. If you have been in continuing contact with some of the other parents you will have much more data to go on. When your youngster realises that you have some information, he is more likely to open up. Information dislodges other information. It will also help you to be aware of omissions in what he says, and of half-truths which may be offered to you.

This process needs a sensitive and candid approach and, if it doesn't already exist, an open-ended dialogue with the youngster otherwise it will seem like interrogation. However, if there is a serious drug problem, or the beginnings of one, the matter is urgent and should be treated forthrightly as a very serious matter. Ask about the use of cannabis, alcohol and other drugs. Often, youngsters are relieved that the subject is out in the open, even though they find it painful.

It is preferable that several parents, or as many as possible, take the initiative collectively in organising other parents and educating as many parents as possible. This suggests an organisation rather than an individual family which might result in your youngster being singled out for jibes or even harassment, by his or her peers. But drugs are serious enough to take this risk if sufficient numbers of parents are not available initially.

Should a drug problem already exist, you should take note of the youngsters who call on or phone your youngster. Peer pressure plays a major role in the spread of drugs and you need to know your youngster's social network. Refuse to allow him to talk to them unless they identify themselves. Also, you should familiarise yourself with the places at which they congregate. You, and the other parents, will need to inform yourselves about the current drugs of abuse as detailed in Chapter 10. You should also consult the school, or schools, and ask if they know of the abuse of drugs.

Parents should now meet again and share what they have learned. When the information is pieced together a much clearer picture will emerge. In addition, now knowing the drug slang you will find that you will pick up clues very quickly.

You must now decide on what steps need to be taken both in the neighbourhood, and in the home. It is preferable that most of the parents broadly subscribe to the protective rules and consequences they will apply to their children for drug related behaviour.

The first important consideration must be the decision that no cannabis, alcohol or any other drugs are allowed. As mentioned earlier, there can be no compromise on this issue. Some will want to add cigarettes too, but you should avoid sophistical discussions about which is more harmful. It would also be worthwhile to make your feelings about lying known. Try to reach general agreement on consequences for drug-related behaviour.

The following are some of the areas that need exploring. The time youngsters return home at night; phone callers should identify themselves; if nowhere particular to go to, the youngster stays at home; places, and groups where drugs are available should be out of bounds.

Parties, concerts and other outings should be supervised or, if not, forbidden. There will, of course, be a howl of dismay, but until the situation is resolved, there is no other way. If a youngster is invited to a party, contact the parents involved and ask about supervision, and what rules there are about drugs and drinking. You can offer to assist. If there will be no supervision, then the party is a hazard and it is preferable that your youngster does not go to it.

Meanwhile, as suggested in Chapter 6 give clear reasons for your anti-drug stand. Inform your youngsters why you feel so strongly, i.e. the damaging effects on growing, developing youngsters of cannabis, alcohol, etc.

The situation may lead you to re-examine your own habitual use of alcohol, tablets and cigarettes in the light of what you have learned, and as an example to your children. Explore the harmful effects of drugs with your youngsters.

If it is necessary to "ground" youngsters, don't leave them with nothing at all to do. They should, of course, have tasks to perform in the home. But, instead of leaving a vacuum encourage youngsters to participate in more involving, healthier forms of entertainment. Pool your ideas with other parents and research others. But, always check on the environment regarding accessibility to, permissiveness about, drugs and drinking.

Needless to add, these measures will be resented. There may be much wailing and accusations. Gratitude will obviously be absent initially. It will take time to get used to the situation. However, continued contact with other parents should give you the support you need. You can share your anxieties, problems, insights, and maintain your resolution.

It would be appropriate to inform the school authorities and other parish and community organisations and gain their support. The school may present a problem initially. Some school principals may deny the presence of drugs since they, like parents, find it too difficult to admit to the presence of drugs, or simply can't contemplate it. If enough parent groups are active, they will feel less threatened. I believe that most schools will be open and co-operative, but there will be the few who will resist the possibility of drugs in the school. It is, of course, the responsibility of the school to see to it that drugs are not circulated or used on school premises. However, the responsibility for individual drug abuse is the parents' alone.

Having said that, let me explain further. The spread of drugs has taken our society by surprise and understandable ignorance of drugs and how they are distributed, including peer pressure and other factors have made youngsters and parents vulnerable. However, failure to acknowledge the danger at this stage would indeed be culpable. Furthermore, action on the part of the Customs and Excise Service and the Gardai cannot successfully intervene in the informal society of teenagers. Only parents can stem the tide of drugs in this area. If they don't, who else will? I have listened to parents of drug abusing youngsters blaming the professional pushers and complaining that the Gardai were not arresting them. Perhaps a reasonable complaint, but unfortunately, these parents were taking no action to stop their youngsters abusing drugs. They were looking to someone else to solve their problem.

At this point, it would be appropriate to convene larger meetings, and include more parents, of users and non-users. You can, as a group, educate other parents, or your community, about the drug problem.

The task now is to tackle the supply of drugs.

It is not wise or productive to try to tackle the professional drug pushers. You will not succeed and you may even become the target of intimidation and your group will disintegrate in fear. This is the reality. If you do come across worthwhile information, pass it on to the police. Let the Gardai know about drug pushing in your neighbourhood and the pubs and other places where it takes place.

But, you *can* tackle the distribution of drugs in your neighbourhood, because drugs reach children mainly through the activities of older youths who have become addicted and now push drugs to make enough money to purchase supplies for their own use. In fact, it is estimated that an addict will involve at least five others within a year, and frequently a great many more. So drug supplies probably come through local youngsters.

Perhaps you will choose to deal with the alcohol supply first. Keep tight control over your own supplies of alcohol. As a group, ask local merchants not to supply alcohol to underage youngsters. If they don't comply, report it to the Gardai, and make your request again. If there is still no satisfactory response, you will have to consider other measures. You can lodge a complaint against his licence, as well. Often, older youngsters purchase alcohol for the underage group. Find out who they are and approach them and their parents. Make sure that your community is alerted to your stand on the drug alcohol. It may surprise you to know that adults often purchase alcohol for youngsters on being given a plausible story.

Publicans should be asked to check ages and request identification from youngsters. It may be difficult to do, but not impossible. Make sure that the people you approach understand that you mean business. Again, the diplomatic approach is advised. Also, if cannabis and other drugs are being circulated in the local public houses, request action from the publican and report the matter to the Gardai. Be sure to check on what happens and, if nothing is done, put your complaint in writing. Persist until action is taken. Keep a log of the steps you take and the dates of requests that you have made and keep copies of your letters.

Request local gardai to increase surveillance of other known places where drugs are exchanged, such as shopping malls, parking areas, bridges, sports fields, pool halls etc. Your group may want to lobby politicians to have the law relating to sales of alcohol to youngsters changed.

Older teenagers who are pushers

Older teenagers as I have said, are frequently the source of drugs and they are a powerful influence among youngsters. Approach their parents in an honest, sympathetic way and enlist their aid. You could ask them to join your group. If you get no satisfactory response you may need to confront the youngsters themselves. Make it clear that your group will no longer tolerate their activities and that you will take legal steps if necessary unless they stop.

Needless to add, you will have to forbid your youngsters to be in the company of these individuals. The most effective means of dealing with them is to isolate them. Ultimately, your youngsters will reject these older youths. When speaking to your youngsters use them as examples of the damage that drugs can do. Focus your discussions with your children on the desirability of growing into mature, independent and healthy adults, able to make their own decisions on how they will lead their lives.

It will take time for the youngsters to get over their dislike of supervision. While adolescents do need privacy, supervision and other measures are necessary until the danger has been remedied. Continue with your research into permissiveness or accessibility of drugs at other gathering places, such as discos, or places of recreation. Also, continue providing supervision for outings, discos, etc.

Since the youngster will be at home much more than usual, you will have an opportunity to get to know each other better and to explore and evaluate the drug experience.

Often, the homes of parents who are not out working are used for smoking cannabis. Let them know and even give them assistance by looking after their youngsters.

You should try to reach agreement on consequences for breaking your rules. These will differ from family to family but try to get broad agreement so that effective consequences follow violation of rules during this period.

By coming together in this way, many other things about your neighbourhood will become obvious to you. You will in fact be creating a caring neighbourhood where a youngster can't go too far wrong before action is taken. You will also develop a sense of common expectation and values among your children. Even more important, you have an early warning system in action.

In researching the drug environment, it is certain that parents will gain a new perspective on the life style of their youngsters and perhaps come up with alternatives to the drug culture. You can look into activities for youngsters that are more involving, like sports, drama, painting, modelling, etc., activities that tap their creativity and expand the range of possibilities that they can explore.

Some youth clubs provide opportunities for youngsters, but it is possible to conceive of opportunities for service to the community, helping others, and doing projects of value, researching the history of the locality, and community services of many kinds. They need something that transcends the objectives of examinations or getting a job, valuable though these be. There are other possibilities in education for living, and increasing awareness of the natural environment of our country.

One outcome could be a new closeness between neighbourhood families and a much improved spirit in your neighbourhood. Mutual assistance will open up other possibilities in your community. Hopefully, the drug experience and the threat which it poses to the life and well-being of our youngsters will prompt us to ponder on what has been happening, and not happening, in our society. What has been lacking in our approach to life, and in our relationships in our own neighbourhood? Do

we know yet what we want, or where we want to
go?

Chapter 8
Co-Operating
With the School

Co-operation with the schools can be an effective means of combating drug abuse and a parent support group at a school can be an alternative to a parish or neighbourhood group.

Teachers can be a valuable part of an early warning system of detecting drug abuse in its early stages. They may observe changes in students and deterioration of an individual's performance long before parents do. However, parents must appreciate that teachers are often reluctant to alert parents to the possibility of drug taking. Frequently initiatives on the part of teachers in this area invite hostile, rejecting and accusing reactions from offended parents. Understandably, teachers become very cautious. In addition, some principals may echo parental attitudes and be most reluctant to admit even the possibility of the presence of drug abusers in a school. These attitudes on the part of some parents and some principals are in fact, aspects of the drug problem.

It is also important to understand that school principals or teachers should not be expected to solve family and community drug abuse problems. However, as a part of the community concerned with young people, schools should participate in preventive action, and in keeping drug abuse out of school facilities.

School Agreement

A parent support committee, in the absence of parent-teacher organisations, can help school principals by devising and publicising among parents a parent-school agreement on how to handle youths who are using drugs/alcohol, and in initiating an early warning system. By circulating or publicising such an agreement among parents, the support committee could define where parents' responsibility must take over, and the concerned response expected of parents.

For example, should a teacher advise a parent of his/her suspicions, parents should be asked by the support committee to welcome this initiative and not to mis-interpret it as a condemnation or an accusation. Suspicion, information, questions or concern coming from teachers should be welcomed. Experience suggests that there will always be some parents who will react with hostility despite the best efforts of the support committee, nevertheless if the majority are sensibly concerned, the support committee's work will be effective.

The support committee would provide an excellent opportunity for parents and teachers to openly discuss the problem of drugs/alcohol amongst youngsters, and become an active force in combating unhealthy adolescent behaviour and encourage the healthy development of youngsters. They could also discuss strategies and responsibilities in responding to the problems.

Information

As suggested for parents acting in the home, the members of the support committee should familiarise themselves with current drugs of abuse and the behaviour and trends of youngsters abusing drugs. They need to be better informed than their children about drugs.

They could explore the availability of outside resources to help them in their work. To be really effective, the committee would need to collect data on the extent of drug abuse in the community, types of drugs, sources, and the preventive measures that are being taken. It would also be instructive in identifying the extent of the problem if they investigated the real level of concern about drugs/alcohol in their community. What are current attitudes, willingness to face the problem, fears, etc.? To what extent are parents unrealistically depending on school authorities, the police and others to solve the problem?

The support committee could seek the support of other organisations within the community, religious, fraternal, etc. The members could also find out what agencies exist to combat drugs and treat and rehabilitate drug victims. The committee could also support teacher training in this area.

School Programme

Inevitably, there is a demand for drug education in schools. It seems logical to insist that this subject be part of a school curriculum. There is a great deal of disagreement in this area as to the advisability of such programmes. Simply warning youngsters against drugs doesn't work, and may even be counterproductive. Including drugs in a health and growth programme might be feasible, or as the subject of an information, evaluation, decision-making and value clarification process. In short, drug education needs to be integrated into a wider context to have any chance of success.

However, drug education in schools cannot be an isolated endeavour. It must be part of a home-based effort to convince adolescents that drugs are self-defeating and destructive and that life has better things to offer than drugs and go on to make sure that it has something better to offer them. It must also include facilitating them in developing self-confidence and personal initiative, responsibility for their own well-being, and in acknowledging their responsibility to the wider community.

Before dealing with measures which the committee might take in the community, let's consider some key considerations in the committee's policy. For example, they must recognise the right to protection of these youngsters who do not use drugs and who may unwittingly be involved in illegal activity; the right of youngsters suspected of drug abuse to help, and to be prevented from committing illegal acts. Also, the teachers have the right to protection in their work. Nor can they be expected to act as a police force.

What of the youngster who is clearly identified

as abusing drugs? It would be easy to expel the youngster. However this might push him/her out of the school system. It would be better to consult with the parents and suggest that they contact the National Drugs Advisory and Treatment Centre, Jervis Street Hospital, and start the youngster on a treatment programme. You need to differentiate between the naive experimenter, the drug abuser and the teenager who is addicted and selling drugs. The naive experimenter can be handled in the home and in co-operation with the school. The other two require treatment and other measures. Contact with the Coolemine Family and Friends Association will be of great benefit to the parents whatever the outcome of measures taken with the youngster.

If the youngster is out of control and cannot be persuaded by his parents to take treatment then, out of consideration of the rights of other students, the dependent teenager should be expelled or, even better, suspend him until such time as he has successfully taken treatment and can resume his studies. This would enable him to stay within the school system.

In suggesting the latter option, I am hopeful that Coolemine Lodge Therapeutic Community will in the near future, have a residential treatment facility for seriously addicted adolescents between 13 and 18 years of age. As said earlier, the experimenter or person involved in a minor way with marijuana or alcohol can be dealt with in the home with back-up advice and guidance from the

National Drugs Advisory and Treatment Centre, and the Coolemine Family and Friends Association. Those at a further stage and youngsters who are becoming delinquent and/or dependent on drugs could benefit from an Outreach or Day Centre, but youngsters who are really addicted, particularly to heroin, need a residential programme.

If no parent support group exists in the school, the principal should use the incident to alert other parents, without naming the offending youngster, and suggest the Parents Action and Prevention Programme outlined in these pages. This would be the most effective means of preventing further drug activity at the school. Not to alert parents and to try to deal with the problem in isolation would be to ignore the reality of the situation and take on a function which the school cannot perform.

It would be valuable for the committee to examine the provisions and operation of the Abuse of Drugs Act 1977, what facilities are available, and explore the role of police, justice and health system in dealing with adolescent drug use. Remembering that drug abuse is mainly a psycho-social problem it is very much within the ability of parents to become knowledgeable in this area, and to be competent in evaluating facilities and in identifying needs. "Experts" do not have all the answers, particularly in relation to parenting and the life of the community. It is perhaps one of our major difficulties that we have surrendered too much power and influence to "authorities" and have ceased to be experts in our own lives and consequently experience a feeling of helplessness.

Drug Supplies
If drinking is the problem among teenagers, parents should endeavour to find out where youngsters are getting the alcohol. If it is coming from someone's home, inform the parents and ask them to keep tighter control over the drink in their home. If it is coming from off-licence shops or public houses, approach the owners, assistants and publicans and urge them to exercise greater care and check identifications and certainly not to serve underage youngsters. Similarly, approach older teenagers who may be purchasing drink for the youngsters, and speak to their parents. Publicise a "fair warning" system which should discourage the supplying of alcohol to youngsters. The same action steps described in Chapter 6 apply to both alcohol and other drugs.

In handling drugs/alcohol abuse in relation to a school, avoid identifying the school as a trouble spot particularly with the media. It doesn't help the situation, can cause a great deal of aggravation, and alienate many parents. Co-operating with support committees from other schools, it is possible to use the media to draw attention to an overall problem.

Sample Parent-Teen Guidelines for Circulation to Parents
These guidelines concern the shared responsibilities of parents, school, teenagers and teachers to each

other and to the community. They are presented because the Special Committee believes they will help to accomplish our goal of a healthy lifestyle. The Committee understands that in some families the guidelines will be too restrictive, in others, too permissive. Nevertheless, they suggest fair and reasonable standards which, it is hoped, will be adopted by concerned parents.

1.   *School.* Everyone needs to be aware of, co-operate with, and support school regulations and rules. Parents and students should pay particular attention to policies concerning absences, tardiness, detention and homework, etc.

2.   *Social life outside of School*
A.   Curfews are necessary for safety and co-operation within each family and among families. The following are suggested:
     School week — Home after evening meal, except for specific event approved by a parent.

     1st and 2nd year Sample Curfews
     Weekends
     —   1st and 2nd year   Home by: . . . .
         3rd year   do: . . . .
         4th, 5th and 6th year   do: . . . .

     Holidays — Home by: . . . . . except weekends as above, with reasonable exceptions.

B.   *Parties* should be chaperoned by adults who are occasionally visible. Alcohol and other drugs should not be available, or served.

Guidelines for agreed rules

Small parties should be encouraged; anyone with alcohol or drugs should be told to leave the premises; parents should feel free to contact host parents and offer assistance; parents should have the telephone number and address of the party, and should expect a call from their teenager in case of any location change.

In addition, parents and youngsters should know where to reach each other by phone. It is advisable that parents be awake (or expect to be awakened) when a teenager comes in at night — this time is an opportunity for open communications. It would also be very beneficial if parents get to know the parents of their youngster's friends. Parents are urged not to treat lightly the use of alcohol, marijuana, or any other illegal drug by their teenagers, and to learn drug-use symptoms! Remember that appropriate, consistent discipline indicates concern for and love of teenagers.

Warning: Don't Go Overboard

It is easy for any group of concerned people to develop unhealthy tendencies. Support committees should be on their guard and curb self-righteousness, belligerence or any activity that is likely to damage the goodwill for their preventive programme. There may be situations or people who do not respond to a diplomatic approach, and firm action has to be taken. Plan such action carefully and as wisely as you can. Keep the organisation non-puritanical and emphasise the healthy development of youngsters through maintaining a non-drug orientated community environment.

Don't Back Down, Either

It is possible that despite the accumulating evidence of widespread drug abuse and the threat that this constitutes to teenagers, some people will see you as cranks or as alarmists. If so, remember that these "do-nothing" people, the deniers, are part of the drug problem. If *you* don't take action, no one else will.

Trust in Community Action

The responsibility for the spread of drug abuse is largely a community one and it will be solved in the community, if it has the will. Teachers can be of great help both in giving an early alert of trouble and in relating the work of youngsters to society. Certainly, training for a life of self-reliance, self-confidence and responsibility can benefit the individual and society if it is incorporated in the curriculum of schools. But this cannot be fully effective unless supported in the home. However, schools can expose youngsters to new dimensions in living and the breaking of old, habitual patterns of thinking and behaving. It could balance the traditional emphasis on the cognitive, the thinking and learning process with awareness of the physical, emotional aspects of being and on re-awakening interest in sensing, seeing, hearing, touching, smelling, testing; in interpersonal relationships, and respect for an individual's essential worth as distinct from the value of achievements. In short, young people need education for living a full life as well as training for earning a living.

The drug problem clearly indicates to us that all is not well with our society, the way we live, our philosophy, our expectations.

Chapter 9
An Addict in the Family

When a youngster becomes addicted, his family becomes familiar with strange attitudes and behaviours. He becomes very demanding, tells an unending string of lies, makes an equally long string of empty promises to get what he wants. He manipulates and exploits the family and everyone else he encounters; he takes no responsibility for his actions or his condition, he blames everyone, the "system", the church, the government, and particularly his parents, making them feel guilty; he avoids facing all problems and displays an intense hostility towards his parents which they find shattering.

He uses every possible strategy to get money from the home and he steals everything he can sell. If parents have credit accounts, he will use them, forge family cheques, use friends and acquaintances of the family to get money.

In search of drugs, he will visit doctors known to hand out prescriptions, and try others with fake complaints. He will try to steal pages from the doctor's prescription pad so that he can forge prescriptions. Some young addicts may even appear at a hospital emergency department faking great pain in the back or some part of the body. After a week of expensive tests and pain killing drugs he will depart. I met one 22 year old several years ago who had put on this act at nearly all the hospitals in Dublin. When they are finding it extremely difficult to obtain money for their drugs, a minority of addicts may seek detoxification, expressing a desire to "kick the habit". When detoxified they will start again on drugs, probably heroin, but they will now need far less money since their tolerance for the drug has been temporarily reduced.

He is likely to break into chemist shops, hospital pharmacies, anywhere he believes he can get drugs. Shoplifting, mugging, intimidation, forging cheques, breaking and entering, all varieties of crime are possible. Under the cover of his new identity as a drug addict no holds are barred. He is now a far cry from the youngster his family once knew. Parents are of course horrified at this hostile, devious, unprincipled person, yet they hope that it will pass, that he will get out of it.

By this time he has moved a long distance from his early drinking and cannabis days. He probably has passed through snorting cocaine, onto weight reducing drugs, barbiturates and other similar drugs and is now "hooked" on heroin. All this time, he may continue to smoke pot and drink.

He is probably injecting heroin into his arms and has his kit of matches, a spoon, cotton wool and hypodermic syringe. He may also use metal bottle caps to dissolve substances for injecting into his veins. His need for a fix is very pressing and he doesn't care how he does it so long as he injects the substance into his veins. Consequently any water to hand is used and it is often water from a toilet bowl, or from a laneway puddle. If you can imagine a young man, any age from 12 upwards, or woman, in a public toilet cubicle sharpening a hypodermic needle with a matchbox, and then drawing water from the toilet bowl, you have an idea of his life style. He may even witness the death of a companion through overdosing. His first reaction will be almost certainly to search the dead person's pockets for money or drugs. It is important to understand that this is the level on which the addict operates. He has no scruples and is totally self-absorbed. His compulsion drives him on and that is all that matters. Witnessing the death of a friend does not frighten or deter the addict. His sole preoccupation is getting his next fix.

By this time he may be running out of accessible veins having exhausted his arms and legs then his feet, and he will probably be injecting into veins anywhere he can find them in his body.

Almost certainly he will develop hepatitis (and he will appear jaundiced) from sharing infected hypodermic needles, resulting frequently in progressive liver damage.

He will lose a great deal of weight and may look scruffy. The hepatitis in itself may lead to liver failure and early death. It is also probable that he will have overdosed several times and has been taken to hospital, if he is lucky enough to be found. Sometimes addicts overdose through trying increasing dosages to achieve a "high" since most of the time they barely reach a kind of normality, with ever increasing quantities of heroin.

It is fairly certain that he has been "cutting" (diluting) heroin in order to sell it to others. He is in fact a "pusher". As I mentioned earlier, drug addicts create addicts.

If you think that you can imagine what is happening to his family, please believe me that your imagination is falling far short of the reality. Apart from the constant fear for his life, there is the hostility, aggression in the home, his long unexplained absences, strange callers and his attitude towards the family. If he is a big youngster he may ruthlessly bully, intimidate and assault members of the family or smash up the home. He may even instal his girlfriend in his bedroom if he has succeeded in dominating the home. I am thinking of several homes where that has happened. Then there are the visits by the police.

Parents move from constant fear for the life of their son or daughter, to despair and often hate for what he is doing to himself and to the family. Their feelings are confused as they gradually realise that they are helpless in the situation and seemingly can only stand by and watch what is happening. The Coolemine Family and Friends Association welcomes parents in this dilemma. Other members who have been through this experience or are going through it will give the new parents understanding, knowledge and support, and advice on what to do. Parents usually find it a life line and experience profound relief.

There are no longer ideal or clear-cut solutions open to the afflicted parents. They should consult the National Drugs Advisory and Treatment Centre for advice and guidance. Obviously, the best possible solution at this stage would be that the addict goes to the Drug Centre in Jervis Street for treatment, including detoxification and counselling and then go on to Coolemine Lodge Therapeutic Community for rehabilitation. Getting him to do this is obviously no easy task.

He will have innumerable objections and excuses. Often addicts claim that the Drugs Advisory and Treatment Centre at Jervis Street Hospital will give information to the police. This is, of course, quite untrue. Treatment is completely confidential, as it would be for any medical problem. Similarly, he may paint a picture of Coolemine Lodge as something of a concentration camp. Since the majority of the Coolemine Lodge staff are trained recovered addicts who have graduated from the programme, they are not as easily manipulated as parents and others have been in the past. Consequently the addict fears the glare of reality and the standards of truth, honesty, openness and confrontation insisted upon in the programme. He knows too that he would not be able to play his victim role and place responsibility on everyone but himself.

Unwilling to give up drugs, the only motivation he will possibly have for seeking treatment is escape from something worse, like the prospect of a substantial prison sentence, realisation that his liver is collapsing, fear of drug pushers to whom he owes money, or weariness from the daily scramble for money and drugs, and poor health. In his recurring depressions, suicide often seems an attractive option and many try it — some succeed. It may be an attempt to get sympathy, get back at parents and make them feel more guilt. It may be a dramatic gesture, and it may very well be a cry for help.

Only at this extreme stage are many able to reluctantly contemplate treatment and rehabilitation. Even so, their motivation is very low.

What I have described of the life of the addict is a composite of lives of a number of 18 to 22 year old addicts who started drug abuse at 15 years of age. It is not exaggerated. There is no need to exaggerate or sensationalise the lives of addicted people, particularly heroin addicts. The facts of their daily lives are horrific enough.

While all of this is taking place, parents, and brothers and sisters, are under continuous strain, worry, frustration and anger. Virtually every strategy will have been used to help the addict to no avail. At some stage in this progression one parent, sometimes both, will realise that helping the addict as they have been, in the end does not help. The parent may conclude that the family can't take any more and he orders the addict out of the house. Older addicts may refuse to leave, or leave but continue to visit the house to get money, food and clothes.

Being ejected from the home is possibly the first real jolt some addicts get. A place to stay, food, money and clothing has enabled them to spend all their available money on drugs, and to this extent parents have been unwittingly colluding with them, by subsidising their drug taking. More than that, they have probably been shielding them from the consequences of their criminal activities, putting up bail, pleading for them, etc., thereby convincing the addicts that they do not have to take responsibility for what they do.

For many addicts, not all, the crises precipitated by being ejected from home can be the beginning of the road to rehabilitation because they will not contemplate any alternatives to drugs until their drug life becomes worse than the prospect of rehabilitation. A substantial sentence in prison may also convince some addicts that there must be a better way, that they are losers again and again. It is of course, possible that an addict can also get drugs in prison but he is unlikely to get them in anything like the quantity he has become accustomed to using.

Over the past year, the work of the Coolemine Family and Friends Association has enabled many parents to take action at a much earlier stage in a young person's addiction. Also, as a result of the Coolemine Parents Action and Prevention Programme, which provides concerned parents with the real facts outlined here, it is not necessary for parents, drug abusers or addicts, to struggle on fearfully and feeling isolated and helpless. It is essential, too, that parents draw on the experience and guidance of the National Drugs Advisory and Treatment

Centre, at Jervis Street Hospital which is the front line in the battle against drugs.

When a person can be induced to go to Coolemine for rehabilitation he will get his best chance of recovery. Forty per cent of those who go to Coolemine Lodge recover. Some leave and return later to complete the programme. Some will never return.

The question is what are Irish parents willing to do to protect their sons or daughters from a life of drugs, crime and possible death such as I have described?

Let's improve our laws, particularly those related to youngsters drinking, and put the onus on publicans to make sure that underage persons are not served drink. Let's intensify our police work too, but in themselves, these and other measures are not sufficient to solve the drug problem. They are essential and they will help, but only parents can provide the real, enduring answer.

All of the young people whose life style I described here started by drinking, moved on to cannabis (pot) smoking and they believed sincerely that they would never get hooked. Some were even determined never to take heroin but ended up injecting it. None of their parents believed that it could happen to *their* child.

All of this need not happen. If we could stop or reduce underage drinking and pot smoking, the first experience of mood altering drugs, and the first steps into the drug scene, we would take a major stride in curbing drug abuse and addiction.

The Career of a Young Addict

Donal is a drug addict. He is 22 years old. He comes from a comfortable home and commenced using drugs when he was 15. His experience differs in detail from others but his progress from drinking to smoking cannabis and then to heroin is typical of most of the young people who become dependent on drugs. Some details have, of course, been changed to preserve his anonymity. He is one of the fortunate ones. He has made his way with typical reluctance into rehabilitation at Coolemine Lodge Therapeutic Community. With persistence he now has a chance to recover, to grow up and develop in honesty and responsibility, and concern for himself and others. He can help himself by helping others and start life once again with confidence and assurance.

"I just got into drugs when I was 15 with the fellow who lived a few streets away, by starting to drink and then smoke hash (Cannabis). I wanted to be one of the lads. It was the done thing at the time, cool. When I got into hash I thought that it was great, and I didn't think I'd ever get addicted to drugs. Those two years were fairly quiet and I didn't get up to much. I used to hang around ———— where we all used to smoke hash. But when I was around 17 I started getting into opiates, coke (Cocaine) and acid (L.S.D.) and all those kind of drugs. I was smoking hash and it wasn't cool enough. It became an ambition after a while to get on heroin. There is a kind of structure within the drug scene and heroin is at the top. I wanted to get up there. I took hash, acid, coke, valium from home, and then morphine and opiates such as dic (Diconal) and Palfium and all those kind of drugs, and mushrooms and things like that. There were barbiturates, uppers and downers, everything I could find, and mixing them with drink. I started climbing the structure.

"At that time I was stealing from home. I wasn't physically addicted, I didn't need it . . . but I wanted it. I suppose I was psychologically addicted, and it was part of my life at this stage. Come 18, I started getting into heroin and at first I started snorting (sniffing) it at weekends. Then some Friday nights I'd spend all my wages on heroin and I'd always be out of money on a Saturday morning. To get money, I'd steal from shops or write cheques. I also started selling hash and acid and coke around that time and a few months later I was selling heroin.

"I got the heroin from my mates, there are loads of people. When I first started getting heroin I was going up to the bar in ———. At that time it was crazy there. There were two peer groups. There was the young crowd and they'd be smoking pot and sit at one part of the bar. The dope fiends, the heroin addicts, would be over at the other end of the bar. We were always cool and I got into that, and I liked it. It was an identity for me.

"I used to get heroin off some of my close mates who used to score it (buy it) off other people. Then gradually I came into contact with dealers, people I'd go to and buy a couple of grammes or whatever. Then I'd cut it (dilute) and I'd do every-thing I could to make as much money for myself. I'd cut it with glucose or maybe codeine tablets, or barbiturates or anything like that. Sometimes I used flour. I often got into trouble for selling practically all flour.

"At this time I was using nearly all the heroin myself and just selling rubbish. I gave up heroin for a month but I was drinking and smoking hash and taking everything else. I was 18 at that time and when I was around 19 I came in contact with the people in town, kind of heavy people. Slowly but surely I started getting deeper and deeper into it and work was a joke at this stage. I didn't go into work and whenever I did I had dealers calling in leaving heroin for me. Nobody ever sussed it, and nobody knew what I was up to. And I'd spend half the day in the toilet shooting up (injecting) and nobody seemed to know. I'd be going around work out of my head, literally not knowing what I was doing.

"After work I'd go over to a pub in town near Grafton Street and I would sell dope over there and I'd swindle, do a few cheques. I got a cheque book. My mother used to keep some money hidden and I found it. I used it to steal from it and I used to take clothes and things from shops I'd go to, and sell them.

"I became physically addicted and I was 19½ and shooting dope (injecting heroin) and I was getting into all sorts of hassles, like police. I was never arrested but I'd been searched and everything and I had a lot of hassle with them. And it used to be the in thing to do to go out some nights. Everyone was stoned on heroin and smoking loads of hash and we'd go out in a car to Dalkey or somewhere. We'd mess around, maybe vandalise things or whatever. And it used to be great to get a chase by the police. That was our kick at the time.

"Then I really started to go across town. That at first was great because I used to get heroin in packs, £10 packs, and they were huge. I couldn't believe it. So I started getting into that and hanging around with heavy people. I started selling for them and started really stealing from home, anything I could find. My own stuff went first, records, clothes and all that, and then my sister's and my brothers' money, and everything went, literally anything I could find.

"I got up early to meet the postman and get my parents' cheques at the door. In one week I went through £400 alone in cheques, and there was money that I was stealing from other places as well. It really shattered them.

"I was selling dope as well and I didn't realise the consequences. Well, I did and I didn't. I always thought that if I got caught, well, my family will bail me out. I suppose I believed that they really wouldn't ever get anything serious on me.

"I gave up work and I started using my mother's credit card and ripping them off. Then I did a run (to go abroad to buy drugs and bring them back to sell) to Holland and made some money. I only did that the one time because I couldn't keep it together.

"The first time I went into treatment was in August a couple of years ago. I was into heroin about 10 to 12 months. I went to the Drug Centre at Jervis Street Hospital and I got on an out-patient's course. I was gradually detoxed but I was drinking and smoking and taking everything else but heroin. I was under the illusion that this was grand. I was off heroin and getting detoxed and I could just drink and take coke (Cocaine) and everything. I stayed off heroin for four days after I finished, but then I went back.

"When I finished that, I went back to work and at this stage they were getting suspicious because I was taking loads of stuff, plus my wages, plus what I'd steal on the side. When I was around 20, I was living in a flat some of the time. I was spending so much money on dope each day. I'd go in two or three times a day for dope.

"I was like a zombie at this time. I remember one Christmas I went into Jervis Street and I got detoxed in there and I came out. I was meant to go to a place called the Rutland but I split and came back and told my parents that I was grand, I'd stay off dope. That day I went into town and I got some heroin and I was using it again then. And it just went on and on. And I was still hanging around the —— bar now and again.

—— had changed. I was going there and all the younger dope fiends knew me. It was a real boost to my ego to go there. They all thought I was great because I was really heavily into drugs at this stage. I used to sell a lot of drugs there and I got a lot of kids messed up from selling dope. A lot of them are in just as much trouble as I am.

"At this stage I started getting in touch with real heavies in the drug scene. I was on the run constantly because I was promising so much that I just couldn't come up with. I was on the run from everybody. So every day I had to go to different people and then I'd meet the other people and I might get beaten up or I'd make another promise. I was just keeping people off and I was really getting into the soup. People were after my guts at this stage. I just kept shooting dope day in and day out and spending about £150 a day. I was writing cheques and had a credit card.

"There were times that I just wanted to kill myself and I tried. I don't think that I really wanted to. There was a bit of fight in me somewhere. Because if I really wanted to I'd have taken a bigger dose than I did. A lot of it was just attention seeking. I would have loved to go out. At the time it really appealed to me to be found dead with a needle in my arm. One, I'd be out of all this crap and, o.k., I'd have left a load of people behind. But I didn't really care at that stage. Two, maybe people would take pity on me. At that stage, that was all I had left. I felt that at least they'd think something of me.

"I was very hostile. I walked over everyone. I had no respect for anyone. I had no feelings for anyone, my friends who were junkies as well. One moment you'd be talking to them and getting on really well. But if it meant a turn-on you'd rip their throat. You wouldn't have any thoughts on stealing from them, or whatever. You have feelings, but you don't have feelings for other people. You just look after yourself. I made sure that I had dope. I didn't care about anyone else. Best mates didn't matter.

"I started taking heavy risks then and the police were getting on to my parents saying that they had seen me around with some heavy dope dealers and an awful lot of criminals known to the police. To me it was cool. But I still went home for anything I wanted, like meals, to sleep and things. I had to live a kind of dual life. If people were at home I might have to meet them and I wouldn't know where I was but yet I had to keep it together. I went into Jervis Street again. In all, I was in there about four times. Eventually I went to the Rutland for about seven weeks and finished the programme. At the time I found it really heavy. When I got out of there I was convinced that I was clean. I lasted four days and I started drinking and that night I got drunk and shot dope.

"My parents were really suffering. My mother often described to me the visions she had of me being found dead in a toilet with a needle stuck in my arm. It must have been pretty horrible for them, and their friends were telling them stories from other people. But it didn't worry me who knew. I was so far. I was really messed up. It didn't matter. All that mattered to me was my dope. My family didn't matter. My sister and brothers were getting messed up too. There were all sorts of junkies coming to the house, real heavies. And our house was being watched and I was being watched. All the people I was with were being watched. My parents went through real hell. I couldn't really describe what they went through. I'd come home and they'd break down. It was really sad.

"My sister and brothers hated me. They'd find syringes, bits of dope around the house. It was crazy.

"I went back on heroin for about two and a half months. I was really messing up. I got into all sorts of trouble then on the street, and I came to Coolemine Lodge. I didn't want to come in. I came in because I was trapped. I had nowhere to go. My parents said that they'd kick me out of home, and the people out in the street were after me.

"At my job I had all sorts of excuses for getting out. I said I had hepatitis and had to go to the hospital. And everybody swallowed it. They were sick of seeing me in Jervis Street getting detoxed and being in for biopsies and things. The last time they told me they wouldn't take me again but I got back again to come to Coolemine. I had tried doctors to get methadone but I never got it. They were all too straight.

"It was really heavy when I came to Coolemine. I didn't want to be here at all. I knew so many people here from the street. I didn't know what was going on. The way I see it is that up to now I've had such crap in my life that there is no way I'll get out of it unless I do this. I don't know what's ahead but I keep going. I left a trail of destruction behind me. If I was to go into the nitty gritty, the crap I put out was too much. I pulled a lot on my parents. I feel really guilty about them. They are so good. Still they love me and would do anything for me. They're out collecting for Coolemine now. It's too much just to see them, the things that I put them through, for me.

"Things happened that you couldn't imagine happening, things you'd see on the T.V. But I was up to it as well, and the sheer frustration I went through trying to give up heroin. Not only that, but every day I'd wake up sick and I'd know I'd have to go out but that I didn't want to. I'd have to because I'd be physically sick and be in bits. I'd crawl down the road and into town. And there would be days when I had no money and I would not know what to do and I'd literally want to throw myself under a bus rather than go around hustling and everything like that. Looking back on it, it's sick really. I did myself a lot of damage. The way I went up the drug structure from hanging around the ———— bar at 15, the place to be. The places I moved to and the people I met, and eventually ended up so messed up. I couldn't handle it. I was just like a zombie. I'd lost everyone and everything and all my respect. I don't know how I did it.

"I discovered at Coolemine that I have abilities that I'd never thought I had. Outside I never did anything. I'd lost all respect for myself. To think that in here now I'm doing things for myself."

When Donal started drinking and using Cannabis at the age of 15 it might have been stopped if his parents had the knowledge that is available today. If they had been able to recognise the danger signals, and knew what to do and how to do it, it is possible that all this suffering might not have happened.

Chapter 10
Life at Coolemine

When an addicted person arrives at Coolemine
Lodge Therapeutic Community, it matches none of
his dire anticipations. The front door is open and
unguarded. He can leave whenever he wants to. But
before he is accepted into the community, he must
convince 5 or 6 representatives of the senior
residents and a staff member that he is serious
about working for his recovery. This takes place at
the Interview. He can hardly believe it when one of
the interviewers, a one-time street mate, starts
asking about the way he lived off his parents and
calls it "acting like a baby". Another former pal
makes it clear that their old street relationship is
over. "We don't need you, but you need us", he is
told. Let's call the new resident Tony. He will have
to earn his place in the community. He finds the
Interview the toughest thing he has faced in a long
time because these residents can see through his
"acts" and tell him so when he uses one of his
customary excuses, or rationalisations. Finally, if
he is accepted, the atmosphere changes. The interview leader says, "Welcome to the family", and the
now smiling residents put their arms around him,
welcoming him and giving him encouragement.
 He first goes into Orientation and learns the

rules, norms and expectations of the House. "The two fundamental rules are, No drugs and no violence or threats of violence. If you break either of them, you will be expelled and you will never be taken back". He joins the kitchen department as a crew member. The department head was also a street mate, but he too is a different person. Instead of the languid dosser Tony remembers, he is all business, issuing instructions and pushing to get the work done. The new resident can't grasp what is going on. He is sure that it's a big con game. They must be shooting dope on the sly. A "heavy" he once knew on the street comes through the door with a clipboard in his hand and briskly gives instructions to the department head, and looks around the room taking in what everyone is doing. He is an Expeditor and among other things he is assessing and recording the mood of the house. He is a long way up the hierarchical structure and has clearly defined responsibilities, prestige and privileges that go with the job. Tony's companion in the kitchen remarks, "I was an expeditor up to two weeks ago when I landed back in the dish pan".

Tony learns that if he wants anything he has to go to his Department Head, then up the structure to a Co-ordinator and then to the staff. To his mind this is weird. Like other addicts, Tony failed to handle the structures of the outside world, the rules of living in the society of other people. And now he is faced with another structure the rules of which are clearly spelt out. In learning to cope with its procedures and rules he will also face his own feelings and low frustration tolerance.

Tony gets up at 7.00 a.m. and God knows when in the distant past he did that before. With his companions, he starts preparing breakfast for the family.

An expeditor will inspect the rooms and if everything is not in trim, including the beds, they will have to be done again and someone may end up "on the mat".

At 8.30 a.m. the family comes together for Morning Meeting. A resident reads The Philosophy,

We are here because there is no refuge finally from ourselves. Until a person confronts himself in the eyes and hearts of others, he is running . . .

Then a co-ordinator delivers the morning "pull-ups", lights left on and so forth. Next the instructions for the day are given by the co-ordinator while a staff member looks on. Quite quickly the mood changes. Someone has started a song and all join in. Then he returns to the kitchen for his department meeting. There is intense activity in the House as schedules are prepared and reports are made at the meeting of department heads. Finally, the "hand over" to staff takes place. All departments are again busily at work until coffee break and then lunchtime, and the day goes busily on.

That evening Tony takes part in an encounter group. A staff member reads out the names of residents who have "dropped a slip" on others. If a resident becomes angry at someone on the floor he can't do anything about it at the moment but he can write his name on a slip with the name of the other person and drop it into a box provided for this purpose in the hall. When the names are read out at the encounter group the writer is free to challenge the offender as strongly as he likes. But he mustn't leave his seat or make threats. Residents can also "drop a slip" on staff members including the Director, if they think that they have been treated unfairly, or given an unwarranted "haircut" (a verbal dressing down). Eventually other residents join in and both protagonists get feedback from their peers which enables them to get a perspective on what they are doing.

And so the life of the community goes on with its checks and balances, rewards and punishments, each resident rising up the structure as he earns advancement and privileges. Tony arrived confused, hurting and resentful. Now he is physically healthy once again. Coolemine Lodge has a permanent problem with jeans and overalls. New members usually arrive undernourished, underweight and in very poor physical condition. A month or two later they have put on weight and their clothes don't fit them any more.

Tony attends other groups and counselling sessions. Because of the structure and pressures of the programme his old self-defeating attitudes, his low frustration tolerance, his habitual responses, rationalisations and excuses come to the surface and have to be dealt with. He begins to relate to his real feelings and for the first time share them with others. He begins to grow, relating openly and honestly with fellow residents and staff, and taking responsibility for his actions and choices — and for the well-being of others. "We help ourselves by helping each other". He cares enough now for his fellow residents, not to cover up if he sees someone "going off the rails".

Tony sees some people "split" — i.e. leave the programme. They are usually aware of turning their backs on the chance of recovery. Usually they fall back on the old victim role, "how could I stay in such a terrible, unreasonable place?". Many subsequently return because life on the street is no longer the same for them. When they return they also acknowledge, at a meeting of the whole family, the hurt they caused to their peers in the community. They make a symbolic commitment to the community. It is all too easy for an addict to say "I'm sorry". He has said it thousands of times to get himself off the hook. Now he has to demonstrate that he means it.

He begins to take a stand in his life, shed his self-preoccupation and to really care for others.

After approximately 12 months he will have earned the role of Head of the House, a position of great prestige and privilege. He will, at his own request, and the evaluation of the staff, advance to Re-entry, the process of returning to society which lasts approximately 6 months.

He will live in a now somewhat overcrowded

house elsewhere in the grounds. Where before he was concerned solely with life in the community, he now starts looking outside to build up support networks of friends, a job, hobbies, etc. He is also testing outside reality once again. There is a great deal of personal work to be done in Re-entry and in many ways it is the most difficult part of the programme. When he passes through it successfully and gets a job, he starts living a new drug-free life. He can graduate 18 months after he leaves if he is still drug/alcohol free and is living a responsible, self-supporting life. If he is suitable, he may return for training and eventually become a staff member ready to help others help themselves.

The Coolemine Therapeutic Community

Coolemine Lodge is a concept-based residential, drug-free therapeutic community. It is an independent voluntary organisation. Coolemine deals with problems of addiction to drugs/alcohol, as a personality disorder that does not respond to traditional psychiatric methods and cannot be cured by transferring the person's dependence from one drug to another. Substance abuse is seen as a symptom of a personality or character disorder that affects the entire person. It has been in operation since 1973; its new programme was introduced in 1981. Coolemine Lodge believes that to assume that addicts are helpless and incapable people ultimately deprives them of the opportunity to take part in their own recovery, and to take responsibility for themselves.

Since Coolemine Lodge regards many of the difficulties as resulting from faulty growth and learning, it re-instructs residents and teaches them better ways of behaving. It also seeks to change the resident's identity as a drug addict to a new one, that of a responsible citizen. Hence the concern with dress, speech etc., breaking with all aspects of the drug culture. The programme provides a new family experience in which the resident is re-cycled, as it were, through the growing up process. Residents are usually in the 18 to 30 age group. The programme accommodates thirty residents in Phase 1 and ten in Re-entry.

The primary objective is to help the resident cope with reality without drugs, foster communication through new interpersonal relationships, reduce anxiety and criminality, provide insight into personal problems, and motivate and encourage change. The process demands that each resident strives with his peers for honesty, openness, concern for others, leadership. It is Coolemine's experience that the outcome of treatment is directly related to time spent in the programme. Even though some individuals do not complete the entire therapeutic process, their behaviour is influenced by the experience.

Why Stay?
The caring atmosphere and obvious concern for one another is the binding spirit at Coolemine Lodge and makes possible the painful confrontation of destructive behaviour, the discipline of the

community, the soul searching, the challenge to grow up. Coolemine believes that man is not fragile, he can confront and be confronted with the reality of his life and grow and develop strength and resources from the challenges of the experience. Residents help themselves by helping each other. "You can't keep it unless you give it away" is an often heard phrase in the community. By talking to each other at first with strain and reservations, but gradually identifying, acknowledging, and risking showing feelings, developing trust in each other, they grow.

Within Coolemine, the individual re-encounters himself. Without the aid of drugs he faces life once again. He can either fight or run. Certainly, he cannot escape into his original solution of withdrawing or becoming detached. He is involved with other people every hour of the day. And he begins to face the challenge of his feelings, the problems of adolescence which he obliterated by abusing drugs. He has to face the problems of growing up, of responsibility for himself and his actions, his feelings and relationships with others, of using his own resources instead of manipulating others into doing for him what he is capable of doing for himself. There is no free ride, no free meal. He earns his keep. Rationalising and creating stereotypes to blame for his condition doesn't work in this environment. He is finally facing what he actually does and the consequences for himself and others. This reality of his being in the world is initially created by his peers and the honest, forthright feedback which they give him. Ultimately, he becomes aware himself of the what and the how of his behaviour and he starts making choices, taking responsibility.

Living in Coolemine he finds a readymade social network which accepted him and which continues to be available when he leaves. He goes through a new family experience which expects, and enables him to grow. In addition, he knows himself, his strengths and weaknesses and what to do about them. He knows what is possible and he has acquired standards which will be difficult, or impossible to ignore or set aside.

Visitors to Coolemine are usually struck by the strong sense of community and the sense of being genuinely cared about by others. Everyone works hard, but the work of each is highly valued and each can see the contribution his work makes to the total functioning of the House. The resident showing you around will tell you, in a tone that indicates that it is his house, that he feels good about it, and what he has done to fix it up.

Helping man to help himself is at the core of the philosophy of Coolemine Lodge Therapeutic Community.

Chapter 11
The Future

If you follow even some of the steps advocated in these pages you will make some discoveries. The first will be that you will have achieved a great deal more than you ever believed that you could. And there will be benefits for your community beyond your initial objective of combating drugs. Your second discovery will be that you have become an expert on the drug problem in your own neighbourhood, parish or community. When you are well on the way in tackling the drug problem in your streets, I believe that you will be impelled by your knowledge and involvement to tackle wider, important issues.

I am thinking of underage drinking. Are you satisfied that the existing laws are being applied as vigorously as they should? If you look at the law relating to youngsters drinking, you may decide that it is inadequate. For example, is the permitted age for the purchase of liquor too low? Should the legal obligation be on the pub or the off-licence owner to make certain that a youngster is not underage? I believe that it should. This is the legal requirement in the U.S., and it is enforced. We can do it too.

If you believe that changes are necessary in this

law, your group can seek the support of local Dáil Deputies. Ask them where they stand. Ask your local councillors for their views. Interest other organisations particularly the Church. Don't be put off. Get commitments and follow them up to see if they are honoured. Get the commitments in writing. Use a questionnaire if necessary and get it signed. Ask your trade union what is its policy on this. Get commitments from them to have the laws changed. Organise your community to get action.

And what of liquor advertising on T.V.? Do you believe that it should still be allowed? If not, say so, and lobby for its removal. You know what's good and bad for your community at this stage.

And what about cannabis? It is an illegal drug, highly damaging to youngsters. It has also become more and more acceptable through ignorance and propaganda by ill-informed adults, and those who want it legalised. Are you satisfied that it is really being treated as an illegal drug? If you smell it in a public house, what will you do about it? Will you stay in the company of adults who smoke illegal cannabis? Will you tell them before you leave that they are creating a market for cannabis and it is consequently getting into the hands of youngsters?

Are you satisfied with the response to drug prevention, treatment and rehabilitation on the part of governments and public health organisations? Let your views be known. Exercise your rights and responsibilities as a citizen.

There is now no reason to believe that if heroin and other currently abused drugs were no longer freely available drug abuse would cease. The illegal use of drugs by young people has been with us for up to 15 years and the idea of altering one's mood with drugs and getting high is now very much part of teenage culture. It will take a long time and considerable effort to eliminate it as a possible activity for teenagers.

Clearly we need to take a long, hard look at our acceptance of the widespread abuse of the drug alcohol as a mood altering substance. We have a staggering number of alcoholic people in our society with all the problems and misery that means in homes, the workplace and in the death of people through accidents. Heavy drinking in families seems to set the stage for youngsters in that family to use alcohol and other drugs.

We must find other more rewarding ways of entertaining ourselves, solving problems and handling life. I believe that if we work at creating better norms and traditions regarding the social use of alcohol we will help enormously in combating drug use. New norms could include attitudes towards drunkenness and heavy drinking at family functions, and celebrations of all kinds. If we succeeded in creating a countrywide distaste for drunken behaviour and excessive drinking we would substantially improve the environment for young people. It would also help those drifting into alcoholism to recognise the abnormality of their use of alcohol at an early stage.

However, our immediate task is to combat and reduce teenage use of alcohol, cannabis and other drugs. It can be done!

Your group can join the Federation of Parents for Drug-free Youth and be kept up to date on the activities, thoughts, and achievements, and objectives of other groups. Your group can provide a speaker or two to talk to other parents and encourage them to take similar action.

Chapter 12
Common Drugs of Abuse

Recognising Drugs

Parents often ask what drugs look like. The answer is simple. Any unfamiliar substance, tablets etc., should be investigated. Parents who say: "I found some pills but I didn't know if they were danger-ous or illegal", are avoiding the real issue. The young people should not be in possession of pills or chemical substances of any kind, except those prescribed by a doctor and therefore, presumably with the knowledge of the parents. All pills, tablets, liquids or other substances which have not been prescribed should be questioned.

Common Signs of Drug Misuse
1. Changes in attendance at work, school.
2. Change from normal capabilities (work habits, efficiency, etc.).
3. Poor physical appearance, including inatten-tion to dress and personal hygiene.
4. Wearing sunglasses (indoors or at night, for instance) usually to hide dilated or constric-ted pupils and also to compensate for the eye's inability to adjust to sunlight. Cannabis (pot) causes blood-shot eyes.
5. Unusual effort made to cover his/her arms in

order to hide needle marks.

6. Blood on shirts, etc.
7. Burnt sheets.
8. Association with known drug users. This is very important.
9. Stealing items which can be sold for cash (to support a drug habit).
10. Unwillingness to communicate at home or to reveal information on his/her activities away from home.
11. Confused thinking, can't tolerate frustration, impulsive reactions, can't seem to solve problems, becoming demanding, hostile, lies.
12. General apathy, loss of interest in previous hobbies, sports, etc.

Identifying the Drug User

A drug user will do everything possible to conceal his habit. So it is important to be able to recognise the behaviour signs, and symptoms of drug misuse. You should be alert to these symptoms, but it is important to realize that the drug problem is so complex that even experts have difficulty making accurate diagnoses. Therefore, it is important not to act hastily since it could lead to falsely accusing your youngster. If in doubt, seek professional help from the National Drugs Advisory and Treatment Centre, Jervis Street Hospital, and the Coolemine Family and Friends Association. Drugs other than opiates can become physically addicting. Some people may acquire an addiction to sedatives and certain tranquillizers. Stimulants in very large doses are addictive.

Terms and Definitions

Drug. Any chemical substance which alters mood, perception, or consciousness, and is misused to the detriment of the individual. Its chemical nature alters the function or structure of the human organism.

Tolerance. Occurs where the body becomes used to the presence of a drug in a given amount, and eventually fails to respond to ordinarily effective doses. Consequently, increasingly larger doses are necessary to produce the desired effects.

Psychological Dependence. May occur as the result of repeated use of a drug. It is a strong desire to continue taking drugs for the sense of improved well-being, or the relief resulting from the absence of tension, anxiety and interpersonal problems. Psychological dependence is much more difficult to treat than physical dependence.

Physical Dependence or Addiction
Occurs when a person cannot function normally without the repeated use of a drug. If the drug is withdrawn, the person experiences severe physical and psychic disturbance.

Harmful Drugs. Every drug is harmful if taken in excess — Alcohol or even Aspirin. Some drugs can also be harmful if taken in dangerous combinations or by hyper-sensitive people in ordinary amounts. The use of alcohol intensifies the effects of many drugs and is used for this purpose.

Slang Terms
To Purchase Drugs: "Score", "Cop", "Do a run".
Sell Drugs: "Deal", "Push".
Intravenous Injection: "Crank", "Fix", "Turn on", "Hit", "Shot".
Syringe and Needle: "Spike", "Works", "Machine", "Artillery", "Arrow", "Spear".

Indications of Possible Misuse
Depressants or Sedatives
Symptoms of alcohol intoxication, but without the odour of alcohol on breath; staggering, stumbling, or apparent drunkenness without odour or use of alcohol; falling asleep while at work; appearing disorientated; slurred speech; pupils dilated; difficulty concentrating.

Stimulants: (Amphetamines — weight reducing preparations — Cocaine)
The person may be excessively active, irritable, argumentative, or nervous. Excitation, euphoria, and talkativeness, pupils dilated; long periods without eating or sleeping; increased blood pressure, or pulse rates.

Opiates: (Morphine, Heroin, Physeptone, Opium, Codeine, Diconal, Palfium, Pethedine)
Marks ("tracks") on the arms or on the backs of

hands, caused by injecting drugs. Occasionally abscesses on arms from injections. Pupils constricted and fixed, possibly dilated during withdrawal. Scratches self frequently. Loss of appetite. Frequently eats sweets, biscuits, and drinks sweet liquids. May have sniffles, red, watering eyes and a cough which disappears when he gets a "fix".

Users often leave syringes, burnt spoons, cotton, needles, metal bottle caps, medicine droppers, in drawers or around the bedroom. The user is lethargic, drowsy, and may go on the "nod" (i.e. an alternating cycle of dozing and awakening). During withdrawal the addict may be nauseated and vomiting. Flushed skin, frequent yawning and muscular twitching are common. Hepatitis (jaundice), is frequently contracted through sharing a "dirty" needle, with resultant liver damage.

Hallucinogens: Marijuana
In the early stages of marijuana usage, the person may appear animated with rapid, loud talking and bursts of laughing. In later stages, he may be sleepy. Pupils may be dilated and the eyes blood-shot. May have distortions of perception and hallucinations.

The marijuana user is difficult to recognise unless he is actually under the influence of the drug, and even then, he may be able to work reasonably well.

The drug may distort his depth and time perception, making driving or the operation of machinery hazardous. Smell of burnt rope in room.

L.S.D.
Behaviour and mood vary widely. The user may sit or recline quietly in a trance-like state or may appear fearful or even terrified. In some cases, dilated pupils. Increase in blood pressure, heart rate, and blood sugar. May experience nausea, chills, flushes, irregular breathing, sweating and trembling of hands. There may be changes in sense of sight, hearing, touch, smell, and time.

It is unlikely that a person who uses L.S.D. for instance, would do so at work, since a controlled environment, often involving a friend to provide care and supervision of the user, is generally desired.

Deliriants: Glue Sniffing
Odour of substance inhaled on breath and clothes. Excessive nasal secretion and watering of the eyes. Poor muscular control (staggering) within five minutes of exposure. Drowsiness or unconsciousness. Presence of plastic or paper bags or rags containing dry plastic cement. Slurred speech. Bad breath.

The Drugs of Abuse
For simplicity, the common drugs of abuse are dealt with in the following pages under the headings:—

1. Opiates or Narcotics
2. Stimulants
3. Depressants or Sedatives
4. Hallucinogens
5. Deliriants

1. Opiates/Narcotics/Analgesics

Morphine, Heroin, Physeptone, Opium, Codeine, Diconal, Palfium, Pethedine, Omnipon, Distalgesics.

Morphine

Medically, a preferred drug for the relief of pain. Morphine is widely used by addicts particularly when heroin is difficult to obtain. It is derived from crude opium. Tolerance builds rapidly.

Form: An odourless, light brown or white crystalline powder. Morphine may appear as tablets, capsules, or in powder form.

Use: Morphine is either injected as a liquid, or taken by mouth. It acts on the central nervous system as an analgesic or pain killer. Traces of morphine detectable by laboratory techniques remain in the body for 6-18 hours.

Signs/Symptoms: Much like those of the more commonly misused drug, heroin.

Heroin (Diacetylmorphine)

Heroin is much more potent than morphine and is a derivative of morphine. The intense euphoria or "high" produced by the drug has made heroin the most popular opiate among addicts. Heroin is similar to all opiate drugs in that tolerance to its effects rapidly develops. As a result, the user must take larger quantities. An individual may begin with a dose of two to eight milligrams but addicts may use as much as 450 milligrams per day as tolerance builds up.

Form: Most often found as an odourless, white, off-white, or light brown powder.

Use: The most common administration is intravenous (mainlining). A drug user's "work kit" is used to convert heroin into a solution. The kit generally contains matches, a burnt teaspoon or small metal bottle cap, medicine dropper, hypodermic needle, and a piece of cotton. The powder is put into a spoon, mixed with water and heated to form a solution. The solution is then injected into the blood stream, generally into the arm. The addict may use his belt as a tourniquet to make a vein stand out. Heroin is also taken by mouth, and is sometimes sniffed or snorted. When injected under the skin, the term "skin popping" is used. The effect is slower and less intense.

Signs/Symptoms: Detectable in body (urine) for up to 10 hours.

Slang: "H", "Junk", "Horse", "Snow", "Smack", "Scagg", "Yak", "Shit".

Physeptone (Methadone)

A synthetic opiate, it is as addictive as morphine or heroin.

Form: A white crystalline powder or tablet or in linctus form.

Use: Most often taken orally in liquid or tablet form. Frequently used in detoxification, to withdraw addicts from heroin.

Slang: "Phy".

Opium (Papaver Somniferum)
The dried, coagulated milk of an unripe opium poppy.

Form: A dark brown, coagulated, plastic-like substance.

Use: Opium may be smoked through a long-stemmed pipe. It has for the most part been replaced by its more powerful derivatives, morphine, and heroin.

Analgesics
Codeine (Methylmorphine)
A derivative of morphine, it was commonly available in cough preparations which are subject to abuse. Nowadays, pharmacists exercise great care in supplying these to individuals. Cough bottles are abused for other substances, mainly anti-histamines.

DF118. Distalgesics

Dangers of Opiate Abuse
Abusers of opiates run a great many risks. In comparision to other drugs, opiates, particularly heroin, are rapidly addictive. The rehabilitation of opiate addicts is very difficult and usually requires long-term residential treatment. Continued use of heroin brings about a deterioration of all standards of behaviour. Abusers run a very high risk of overdose and death.

Abusers become extremely careless because of their urgent need for a "fix" and often use "dirty" or infected hypodermic needles for injecting themselves. As a result, a large proportion of opiate abusers contract hepatitis and suffer serious liver damage, often resulting in liver failure.

Because of the increasing sums of money required to finance his addiction, up to £150 per day, addicts inevitably become involved in criminal activities, including selling heroin and other drugs to others.

2. The Stimulants

These are the drugs which produce an increase in bodily and mental activity. They increase the central nervous system's reaction. Users feel alert and confident, tiredness is either temporarily banished or at least feelings of fatigue are less marked. The full intensity of effect depends, as with all drugs, on when and how much is taken and the past experience of the user, or lack of it. The user's immediate mood can increase or reduce the "felt" effects of the drugs.

Some of the reasons for taking stimulants include a wish to "keep going" at all-night discos, or parties, to counteract the effects of drugs of another group which have resulted in a tendency to fall asleep, and because they promote a sense of superiority and confidence.

Popular forms of stimulants in use:
Amphetamine sulphate (speed), Methedrine, Ritalin, Cocaine. *Anorectic (weight reducing drugs)* Ponderax, Tenuate, Ionamin.

Psychological dependence is common in misuse. Abuse of stimulant drugs brings about hyperactivity, talkativeness, hallucinations, a general excitability, including aggressive or anti-social behaviour, or they may feel very frightened and isolated. Continuous misuse of amphetamines may produce a psychosis resembling paranoid schizophrenia with accompanying delusions and hallucinations. Amphetamine abuse can also produce high blood pressure and abnormal heart rhythm. Most types of amphetamines are not now readily available in Ireland.

Some users combine stimulants with other drugs, including alcohol, to experiment with the effects obtained from the various combinations. Excitability and intense paranoia may result from amphetamine injection. There is much greater danger of violent outburst than would occur with a heroin addict. Amphetamine users often stay awake for days without food, undergoing hallucinations and bouts of paranoia, then lapsing into long, deep recovery sleeps. Unlike the "drifting off" effects of heroin, injected amphetamine creates a flash or high and an illusion of heightened mental power.

Amphetamine Sulphate (speed)

Use: Amphetamines ("Speed") are used as tablets, capsules, and in solution for injection. The toxic dose of amphetamine varies, depending upon the individual. Increased dosages are continually made in order to

> obtain the desired effects. Period of detect-
> ability in body fluids is 24-36 hours.

Cocaine (Erythroxylon Coca)

Cocaine is also prohibited under the Misuse of
Drugs Act 1977. Cocaine is a potent central
nervous system stimulant and therefore it is in no
way similar to heroin or morphine, which are
opiates. It is a stimulant similar to the amphetamines. At one time, cocaine was widely used as a
local anaesthetic, but it has now been largely
replaced by synthetic substitutes.

Form: On the illegal market, cocaine appears
generally as an odourless, white, fluffy
powder. A line of "coke" costs about £30.

Use: Cocaine is generally sniffed and is absorbed
through the mucous membrane of the
nose. It can also be injected intravenously,
directly into the bloodstream. The result of
either method is a strong stimulation of the
central nervous system. One well-known
method is to combine cocaine with heroin
into a powerful injection known as a
"speedball". Morphine is also used in
combination with cocaine.

Signs/Symptoms: User appears to have euphoric
feeling and be energetic. Pupils are dilated
and fixed. Tremors may occur. The
euphoric sensations are short lived and
quickly replaced by feelings of anxiety and
depression, sometimes accompanied by
hallucinations and paranoid delusions. The

user may express a feeling of superiority. Regular use causes irritation and inflammation of the mucous membrane of the nose, so the user gives the impression of having a severe cold with "blocked" nose.

3. The Depressants or Sedatives

The name refers to the way the activity of body and brain is slowed down. It does not mean that users feel depressed — quite the opposite. Parts of the brain work less efficiently due to the presence of depressant drugs. Consequently, the user is less likely to suffer the full effects of pain, while feelings of anxiety are decreased and sometimes eliminated. However, the CAUSE of pain is not removed nor are the things that cause worry dealt with. The feelings of relaxation and well-being can be intense with periods of pleasure. This is a fairly large group and contains some very well-known and widely used sleeping tablets and tranquillisers.

Antihistamines: Piriton, Phenergan, Cough Mixtures.

Tranquillisers and Sleeping Tablets: Librium, Valium, Mogadon, Ativan, Dalmane, Diazepam, Tranxene, Equanil, Miltown, Noludar, Mandrax.

Barbiturates: Phenobarbitone, Nembutal, Sodium Amytal, Seconal, Tuinal, Soneryl, Luminal.

Alcohol

Most of the drugs listed are available in pill or capsule forms. All of these drugs, except alcohol, are offered in one way or another, on prescription for a range of medical conditions.

Ever increasing doses in search of maximum effect or well-being often lead to overdosing with the possibility of very deep coma or death. Lesser amounts spread over time may lead to dependence and risk of physical damage. All the drugs in this group do not have intensity of effect, but they can all produce unpleasant consequences.

Because of their influence on thinking and behaviour, using these drugs causes special risks. They slow down the speed and accuracy of responses to emergencies, e.g. sudden braking while in a car. Like all psycho-active drugs they interfere with the quality of thought and may lead to making unwise decisions, or evaluations of situations.

Barbiturates

A barbiturate is a sedative and a hypnotic and it exerts a powerful depressant or calming action on the central nervous system. The medical uses for barbiturates are wide including: epilepsy, hypertension, insomnia, nervous tension. Like heroin, they result in physical and psychological dependence. One major danger with barbiturates lies in the withdrawal symptoms which include epileptic-like seizures. Respiratory failure can also occur with withdrawal. Barbiturate addicts must be withdrawn under medical supervision. Convulsions can occur for some weeks after cessation. High doses of barbiturates by addicts can create feelings of elation, tranquillity and well being.

Form: Barbiturates are usually available in capsule or tablet form.

Use: Barbiturates are taken by mouth /intravenously.

Regular doses, over a period of time produce dependence. Barbiturates depress mental and physical functions. Abusers are slow in speech, and slow in action, erratic in judgment. If the drug is not available, an habitual barbiturate user may experience similar reactions to the opiate addict. His body develops a tolerance and he suffers severe withdrawal symptoms. A barbiturate addict may also become overactive and very aggressive under the influence of the drug.

Signs/Symptoms: Slurred speech, staggering, lack of muscular control.

Overdose: Can easily occur particularly if the tablets are taken in conjunction with alcohol which is itself a sedative. Death may occur if the person falls asleep, vomits and chokes. These drugs should never be discontinued suddenly as convulsions may occur during withdrawal. The person concerned should be hospitalised.

Slang: "Barbs", "Downers", "Nemmies", "Yellow Jackets", "Tunes", "Goofballs", "Sleepers" "Blue Heavens".

4. The Hallucinogens
LSD, Mescalin, Peyote, Cannabis (Marijuana),

Magic Mushrooms.

The hallucinogenic drugs, as the name suggests, can produce hallucinations of various kinds. They form a relatively small category. There are two principal hallucinatory drugs generally available: LSD (lysergic acid diethylamide 25) and cannabis. There are others, psilocybin, mescaline, DMT, and STP, but these are not common here.

LSD
LSD is commonly in the form of a spot or "shape" on blotting paper or red star on black paper. The amount of LSD required to induce hallucinatory "trips" is very small, a typical dose being in the order of 100-150 micrograms (a microgram is 1,000,000th of a gram). LSD may vary very considerably in strength, above and below the figure given above. Users experience events in strange ways: in fact, they hallucinate. The effects may be pleasant but some experience highly unpleasant and very frightening effects which can result in severe, usually temporary, mental disturbances.

LSD is one of the most potentially dangerous drugs, not least because of its unpredictability. Experiences can go very wrong and young people are at particular risk, possibly because as immature people they are easily susceptible to suggestion. It is sold at £5.00 per tablet.

Its medical use is extremely limited and it is not accepted for medical treatment at present. Recent studies have indicated that LSD may cause chromosomal damage resulting in congenital birth defects. LSD can produce a feeling of complete detachment from reality and can cause actions that lead to serious injury or even death to users. An LSD user can also become dangerous to others. It is known as a "mind expanding drug" that can "blow your mind".

Use: LSD is generally taken by mouth. Practically any substance such as a tablet, sugar cube, biscuit, paper, etc., can be a source. When LSD was first introduced into the illicit market it was commonly added to a sugar cube. On rare occasions, LSD is injected directly into the bloodstream. The effect of LSD changes the levels of certain chemicals found in the brain, including serotonin, which produces changes in the brain's electrical activity. This may result in hallucinations, the intensification and distortion of sensory perception, panic, violence, suicide, or a loss of sanity. Hallucinations may recur (with the same intensity) any time for several years after the original "trip".

Slang Terms: LSD: "Acid". Mescalin: "Mesc". Peyote: "Peyote Buttons".

Cannabis (Cannabis Sativa), Marijuana, Pot, Hash
Cannabis is currently the biggest threat to adolescents because of the widely held erroneous belief that it is a "harmless" drug.

Adolescents are often insecure and frightened

and they are more vulnerable than they will be at any other time in their lives. Hopefully they will learn how to cope with the anxieties of these troubled years and emerge as healthy adults. Cannabis (Marijuana) however, provides adolescents with a refuge from growing up. Many of the kids huddling over a marijuana joint are opting out, hiding from sexual anxiety, loneliness, personal doubts and other problems adolescents must confront in order to become responsible, self-assured grownups. If they never come to grips with these problems, they will end their teenage years as only partially finished adults without the resources they need to cope with life.

Medical researchers are finding that Cannabis has adverse effects on the lungs, the brain, the reproductive system and the immune system. Cannabis smoke appears to have greater carcinogenic potential than tobacco smoke, does more damage to the lungs' antibacterial defences and interferes more with pulmonary functions. Female cannabis smokers have three times as many defective monthly menstrual cycles as non-users. For male users, cannabis reduces the mobility of sperm and increases the amount of abnormal sperm.

Cannabis also affects judgment, memory, co-ordination and motor skills. For drivers, the effects can be fatal. If children find that marijuana is pleasant, they're likely to go after more powerful "highs" and a growing number of adolescents today are moving on to heroin, cocaine, LSD and other drugs.

Cannabis Sativa, commonly known as marijuana, Indian hemp, or hashish, is an annual, herbaceous plant and has been cultivated for centuries as a source of fibre for making rope, for the oil content of its seed and, more recently, for the intoxicating substances found in its flowering tops. In many parts of the world the plant grows as a weed and exhibits extremely rapid growth, similar to the hops plant, a related species. It is grown illegally in Ireland.

There is a wide variety of cannabis preparations, depending upon the region of the world in which it is grown and used. For the most part, marijuana for use as an intoxicant is prepared from dried mature leaves, dried flowering tops and, in some cases, the entire dried plant. It is usually smoked in cigarette form, called a "joint".

Before 1964, the intoxicating properties of cannabis could not be related to a specific chemical constituent of the plant. In the past sixteen years, however, the complex chemistry of cannabis has been elucidated and much information is now available. The principal psychoactive ingredient is known to be delta-9-tetra-hydrocannabinol (delta-9-THC), although there are least 50 identifiable substances present. Other constituents include delta-8-THC, cannabinol (CBN), and cannabidiol (CBD).

The identification of delta-9-THC in 1964 was the first significant breakthrough in the study of cannabis and represented an achievement similar to the isolation of morphine from the opium poppy, cocaine from coca leaves and mescaline from the peyote cactus. The identification of delta-9-THC as the principal psychoactive component has enabled the pharmacologist and the biochemist to assess quantitatively marijuana's mode of action. Much of the early work dealing with cannabis was conducted with material that had not been assayed for active ingredients or had not been stored under optimal conditions, especially as THC is rapidly inactivated by exposure to oxygen, light, humidity, and elevated temperature.

The intake of 5 to 10 milligrams of delta-9-THC into the bloodstream is held to be sufficient to induce cannabis intoxication. Allowing for the inefficiency of inhalation, one can readily see that a single marijuana cigarette of the drug type is sufficient to induce a cannabis "high".

Hashish is a more concentrated preparation of resinous material found in the flowering tops of Cannabis sativa, and may contain as much as 10% THC. Liquid hashish or "Marijuana Oil" with a potency of 30 to 90% THC is also available and has been characterised as "one of the most frightening drugs on the market today".

Effects of Cannabis
(a) Desired effects: The desired effect of a "normal" dose of THC (i.e. 5-20 mg) is a state of euphoria called the "high" which is characterised by CNS effects such as easy laughing, elation, heightened awareness and relaxation.
(b) Undesired effects: These normal doses also

cause a significant impairment of learning ability, short-term memory and on psychomotor performance. It is generally accepted that normal cannabis use impairs thinking, reading comprehension and the ability to cope with verbal and arithmetic problems. The more complex the task, the greater the degree of disruption produced by intoxication. Most of this impairment, which has direct significance for learning ability in students who use cannabis frequently, is related to interference by cannabis with short-term memory storage.[1]

Eminent scientists from around the world agree that, based on recent findings, marijuana must be considered a very dangerous drug. Available findings suggest that the effects of cannabis are cumulative and dose-related, and that prolonged use of marijuana, or less frequent use of the more potent hashish, is associated with at least six different types of hazards.[2]

1. THC, the principal psychoactive factor in cannabis, tends to accumulate in the brain, and gonads and other fatty tissues in the manner of DDT.
2. Marijuana even when used in moderate amounts, causes damage to the entire cellular process.
3. Tied in with its tendency to accumulate in the brain and its capacity for cellular damage, there

[1] IMJ Vol. 74 No. 10. Corrigan D. School of Pharmacy TCD.
[2] "Marijuana today". Russell G. The Myron Inst. for Adult Education N.Y. and the American Council on Marijuana and other Psychoactive Drugs Inc.

is a growing body of evidence that marijuana inflicts irreversible damage on the brain, including actual brain atrophy, when used in a chronic manner for several years.

4. There is also a growing body of evidence that marijuana adversely affects the reproductive process in a number of ways and that it poses a serious danger of genetic damage and even of genetic mutation.

5. Chronic cannabis smoking can produce sinusitis, pharyngitis, bronchitis, emphysema, and other respiratory difficulties in a year or less, as opposed to ten or twenty years of cigarette smoking to produce comparable complications.

6. Cannabis smoke, or cannabis smoke mixed with cigarette smoke, is far more damaging to lung tissues than tobacco smoke alone. The damage done is described as "precancerous".

7. Chronic cannabis use results in deterioration of mental functioning, pathological forms of thinking resembling paranoia, and a "massive and chronic passivity" and lack of motivation — the so-called "amotivational syndrome".

Signs/Symptoms: Bloodshot eyes, sensitivity to light, (leading to use of sunglasses), enlarged pupils, glassy shining appearance of the eyes. Smell of burnt rope.

Slang: "Pot", "Hash", "Rochy", "Dope", "Draw", "Blow", "Smoke", "Grass", "Weed".

Magic Mushrooms
Mushrooms which grow on high ground are frequen-

tly found on golf courses. These are special strains of fungi, not the common mushroom. They grow from late summer through to winter. They are brown, long stemmed with an umbrella-shaped top.

If eaten in sufficient quantities, they can produce hallucinations — ataxia, inco-ordination and confusion. Its effects are similar but milder than LSD. The mushrooms are eaten fresh or dried and perhaps crushed into a fine powder. There is no information on the lethal dose. Users eat up to 30 or more mushrooms at a time to achieve the desired effect.

5. The Deliriants

Finally, there is a fifth category of drugs, the so-called deliriants. These are a range of substances which include dry-cleaning fluids and solvents. The list of substances in this category includes:

Impact adhesives	Aerosols of various kinds
Dry-cleaning fluids	Petrol
Nail polish remover	Rubber solution
Tippex liquid	Model cement

The most widespread form of misuse in this category is glue-sniffing. The user smears the glue (often impact adhesives) on a tissue or handkerchief and places both handkerchief and head inside a bag and sniffs the vapour. There is a fairly immediate and relatively short-lived feeling of relaxation and well-being. The effects are sometimes boosted by alcoholic drinks and this results in particularly intense and longer-lasting experiences of a kind of drunkenness.

Some users have reported hallucinatory episodes following the use of one or more of the substances mentioned above. In addition to the effects already mentioned, the user may suffer from blurred vision, and there may be confused thinking and loss of memory. At least in the early stages these effects pass off but while they last they are very real and can cause the user considerable anxiety, especially if the experience is intense. Among the hazards of being temporarily out of control is that of being accidentally injured.

The practice of glue-sniffing has already claimed the lives of some young users, and damaged others. Many experts believe that glue-sniffing can damage the liver, kidney, and the bone marrow. It is common to see skin burns and sores around the nose and lips of users. Because the substances are easy to get they pose a serious problem for young people.

Patterns of Misuse of Drugs
Practically all of these substances dealt with here have potential for dependence. If taken over a period, there is a risk that dependence will result with a loss of control and potential damage to health, career, and personal relationships. Loss of control means that the user cannot refrain consistently from taking whatever drugs may happen to be involved. The drugs and other substances discussed vary in their potential to produce

dependence but depressants are the most likely to lead to dependence. Not all drugs produce physical dependence but arguably all drugs can cause psychological dependence, which can also be very difficult to treat.

In serious cases of misuse the pattern may begin by the person responding to life's circumstances by taking drugs. Ultimately the misuser does not wait for a bout of misery or whatever formerly triggered off the drug-taking, but keeps on taking the drugs and so keeps the unwanted circumstances at bay. So, stressed or otherwise difficult lives, coupled with the availability of drugs and a willingness on the part of the troubled person to use them, may unite to form the beginnings of a drug problem. Drug abuse is frequently associated with personality problems.

However, there is not an inevitable progression from worry and avoidance of difficulties, to the use of drink or drugs leading eventually to dependence. The cycle can be broken by the person himself, by his family and by changes in his environment.

Most of those who briefly experiment with drugs will leave this phase behind them but many will become seriously involved and it is not possible to predict who the victims will be.

Example:
If parents misuse drugs, there is a very strong possibility that their children will do the same thing. If a child sees his parent use alcohol or other

drugs as a way of responding to difficult occasions or as a preferred means of entertainment, they will probably absorb that example and respond in the same way. Parents who tackle their problems in a determined and reasonably systematic way are providing good and helpful examples for their children. Homes in which drugs are treated with respect and not given an exaggerated importance demonstrate to the children a healthy attitude to drugs.

Appendix 1
Overdose Emergency

If you suspect an overdose, err on the side of taking immediate action rather than hesitating or worrying about the reaction of the hospital should it turn out to be a false alarm. Ring 999 or call a taxi, whichever you consider quicker. Whether an overdose is accidental or intentional you cannot rely on the person's estimate of the number of tablets taken and anyway, he almost certainly will not know what constitutes a fatal dose of a particular drug so don't take any chances. Frequently people in these situations underestimate the quantities taken. Inform the hospital of the name of the drugs, if you know, and if alcohol is involved. Bring the tablet bottle or bottles with you to the hospital.

You will find some guidance on symptoms of an overdose in the Chapter on Common Drugs of Abuse. However, if the person is unable to stand or shows signs of unconsciousness, or severe withdrawal symptoms, e.g. convulsions, you should get help immediately.

While awaiting help, you could endeavour to keep the person awake by walking him around. If he is unconscious, try and arrange him in the "safe" position by (1) placing him on his side with the underarm extending behind him as comfortably as possible. (2) Then bend the topmost arm placing part of it under his forehead to act as a pillow. (3) This should ensure that his nose and mouth are pointing towards the floor. (4) It is important that you check that his mouth is open from time to time and to ensure that it is not blocked by his tongue, or vomit.

Appendix 2
Treatment, Advice, Rehabilitation

NATIONAL DRUGS ADVISORY AND
TREATMENT CENTRE
Jervis Street Hospital, Jervis Street, Dublin 1.
Phone: 01-748412

COOLEMINE LODGE THERAPEUTIC
COMMUNITY
Coolemine, Clonsilla, County Dublin.
Phone: 01-214545

COOLEMINE FAMILY AND FRIENDS
ASSOCIATION
Coolemine, Clonsilla, Co. Dublin.
Phone: 01-214545

Appendix 3
Cannabis Bibliography

Answering Questions about Marijuana Use
Drs. Ingrid Latner, James O'Brien and Harold Voth.
Patient Care, May 30, 1980. Reprinted by the U.S.
House Select Committee on Narcotics Abuse and
Control, H2 — 234, Hanse Annex 2. Washington
DC20515. Publication SCNAC — 96 — 2 10.

Better Grass
The cruel truth about Marijuana, Roy Hart, Psycho-
neurologia Press.

Cannabis and Health — A Review
Dr. Desmond Corrigan, B.Sc. (Pharm.) MPSI. F.L.S.
Lecturer in Pharmacology, School of Pharmacy,
T.C.D. Irish Medical Journal, Vo. 74 No. 10.
October 1981.

Keep Off the Grass
Gabriel Mahas, Readers' Digest Press, New York,
1977.

Marijuana
An annotated Bibliography, Waller, Johnson,
Buelke, and Turner, Research Institute of Pharma-
ceutical Sciences, University of Mississippi,

Macmillan, New York, 1976.

Marijuana and Health 1980
8th Annual Report to the U.S. Congress, NIDA
Rockville MD20850.

Marijuana — Deceptive Weed
Mahas, Gabriel, G. M.D., Ph.D., Raven Press, New
York, 1973.

Marijuana
The myth of Harmlessness goes up in Smoke.
Peggy Mann. Reprinted from "Saturday Evening
Post" by Medical Research and Research Founda-
tion, Indianapolis.

Marijuana Research Findings, 1980
Robert Peterson, Editor, Research Monograph
Series. NIDA Rockville MD20850.

Marijuana — Time for a Closer Look
Curt Janeczek, Healthstar Publication, Columbus,
Ohio.

Marijuana To-day
Russell, G. The Myron Inst. for Adult Education
N.Y. and the American Council on Marijuana,
Other Psychoactive Drugs, Inc.

Marijuana Update
Peggy Mann, Reprint Editor "Reader's Digest",
Pleasantville NY 10570.

Parents, Peers, and Pot
National Institute on Drug Abuse 1979.

The Legal Status of Cannabis
Dr. Desmond Corrigan, B.Sc. (Pharm.) MPSI. F.L.S. Lecturer in Pharmacology School of Pharmacy, T.C.D. Irish Pharmaceutical Union Review, December 1980.

Appendix 4
Helping Parents
to Help Themselves

**Coolemine Parents' Action and Prevention
Programme**
To help parents to take effective action against the
spread of drug abuse and addiction, training programmes are arranged for groups of parents, or for
a neighbourhood, parish, or community.

After training, parents can educate other parents.
The training programme consists of the following:

1.   Identifying Common Drugs of Abuse.
     Why youngsters take drugs.
     Effects on personality.

2.   A parent's experience of drug abuse in
     the home.

3.   "How I manipulated and deceived my
     parents" — A recovered addict.

4.   What you can do in the home.
     The danger signals.
     Taking action.

5.   Communicating with your children.

6. What to do in your neighbourhood, parish, community, and in co-operation with your school.

Parents, or professionals, who wish to organise a programme for their area should contact:

> Secretary,
> Coolemine Parents Action and Prevention Programme,
> Coolemine Lodge Therapeutic Community,
> Clonsilla, County Dublin.
> Mornings: Phone 01-989893
> Afternoon or Evening: 01-214545

The programme is conducted by experts from Coolemine Lodge and experienced trained parents of the Coolemine Family and Friends Association.

Appendix 5
Guide to Drug Slang

Some of these terms have slipped into common use

ACID	L.S.D.
ACID HEAD	L.S.D. User
AMP	Drug ampoule
AGGRO	Aggression, Disagreement
AMPHETAMINES	Bennies (Benzedrine), Dexies (Dexedrine), Happy Pills, Pep Pills, Sweets, Jolly Beans, Sulphate.
ARROW] ARTILLERY]	Hypodermic syringe with needle. Arrow, Machine, Spear, Spike, Works.
BAD SCENE	Unpleasant, dangerous, un-productive situation or place.
BAD TRIP	Disturbing or upsetting L.S.D. experience.
BANG	Exhilaration or impact achiev-ed through drugs, sexual intercourse.
BARBS	Barbiturates.
BENNIES	Benzedrine. Not readily avail-

	able in Ireland now.
BLOCKED	Strongly affected by a drug.
BLOW OUT	Spill drug while preparing for injection.
BLUE HEAVENS	Barbiturates.
BREAD	Money.
BREADHEAD	A person pre-occupied with money.
BROUGHT DOWN	To lose the effect or "high" of drugs.
BUGGED	Annoyed. "Bugged me" — "He annoyed me".
BULLET	Capsule.
BUM GEAR	Poor quality or phony drugs.
BURN	Steal money or drugs.
BUST	Caught by the Gardai — arrested and charged.
BUZZ	Feeling extra good or euphoric through drug use. Had a "Buzz on".
C.	Cocaine, Charlie, Coke, Snow.
CAPS	Drug Capsules.
CHARLIE	Cocaine.
CLEAN	No visible injection marks on arms, etc., or to have no drugs.
COCAINE	C. Charlie, Coke, Snow.
COKE	Cocaine.
COLD TURKEY	Getting off drugs by suffering the withdrawal symptoms

	without the help of other drugs. Usually refers to heroin withdrawal.
COME DOWN	To come down off the drug "high".
CONNECTION	Contact person for obtaining drugs.
COOK	Dissolve tablet in water in order to inject it into vein. Heating hashish in silver foil prior to soaking tobacco with it.
COOK UP	To heat and dissolve heroin on a spoon before injecting it into the veins.
COP	Purchase drugs, score.
CRACK UP	Burst into laughing. Nervous breakdown.
CRANK UP	To inject drugs.
CRASH	To fall into a drug-induced sleep.
CUT	To weaken a drug, usually heroin, with some other substance in preparation for selling it.
DEAL	To make a deal (to deal), buy or sell drugs, push.
DEXIES	Dexedrine. Not readily available in Ireland and not widely used.

DICKIES	Diconal tablets.
DO A RUN	Get or purchase drugs in England or other European country for use in Ireland.
DOPE	Drugs.
DOPE FIEND	Drug addict. Usually said in mock fashion.
DO-DO'S	Bronchial tablets (Ephedrine and Caffeine).
DOWNERS	Sleeping Tablets, Tranquillisers, Barbiturates.
DRAW	Cannabis.
DROP	To swallow a pill.
FIX	Need a fix — needs an opiate injection. To inject, turn on, hit, shot, crank.
FIXING KIT	Hypodermic syringe, needle, spoon, cotton wool, lemonade bottle cap with cork layer removed.
FLAKE OUT	Flaked out, tired.
FLIPPED	Flipped (his lid), lost control.
FLASH	Effect of cocaine. Also of Methedrine ampoules — rarely available.
FLASHBACK	An L.S.D. experience, usually unpleasant or unnerving that may happen to the person even years after he has stopped using L.S.D.

FLUSHING	Sucking blood back into a syringe to ensure that all the drug is being absorbed.
FREAK-OUT (to freak out)	Lose control or to hallucinate on L.S.D. or speed (amphetamines).
GEAR	Drugs.
GONE	Intoxicated.
GOOF-BALLS	Barbiturates.
GOOFED UP	High on barbiturates.
GRAMME	A gramme of any drug.
GRASS	Cannabis. A squealer (informer).
GREEN AND BLACKS	Librium.
H	Heroin, Junk, Horse, Snow, Smack, Scagg, Yak, Shit.
H & C	Heroin and Cocaine (Smack and Charlie).
HABIT	Addiction.
HARD DRUGS	Heroin.
HASH	Hashish (Cannabis Resin).
HASHISH	Cannabis Resin.
HASSLE	To harass, trouble, bother, nag, push.
HEAVY	Heavy situation: dangerous, aggressive situation.
HEROIN	H, Horse, Junk, Scagg, Shit,

	Smack, Snow.
HIGH	Drug induced euphoria, excitement.
HOOKED	Addicted to drugs.
HORSE	Heroin.
HUNG UP	Disappointed in getting drugs, down, obsessed with.
HUSTLE	Selling.
HYPO	Hypodermic syringe.
JOINT	Cannabis cigarette. Usually hand rolled.
JUNKIE	Addict.
KICK	Thrill.
GOING ON A KICK	To embark on a drug taking episode.
KICKING	The process of giving up the use of drugs (Kicking the habit).
LAY ON	To give or get drugs on credit.
LEBANESE RED	Cannabis Resin originating in the Lebanon.
LEBANESE GOLD	Cannabis Resin originating in the Lebanon.
LOADED	Loaded with money. Also loaded with drugs.
L.S.D.	Lysergic Acid Diethylamide.

Acid.

M	Morphine.
MACHINE	A hypodermic syringe.
MAIN LINE: MAIN LINER	Injecting drugs, usually heroin, into the veins, a person who injects drugs into his veins.
MANDIES	Mandrax tablets.
MARIJUANA	Cannabis, Joint, Reefer, Smoke, Stick, Pot, Hash.
MARY-JANE	Cannabis (Marijuana).
MESC	Mescalin.
MICRO-DOT	L.S.D. in the form of coloured dot fixed on paper. Also many coloured tiny tablets. L.S.D. has not been widely used in Ireland since the early '70s, but there are indications that it is regaining popularity.
NEEDLE	A hypodermic syringe needle.
NICKED	Caught by the police, arrested
NOD	A sleepy state induced by drugs.
O	Opium.
OPIUM CHARGE	Cannabis impregnated with opiates.

OUT OF YOUR MIND	High level of intoxication, or "you are wrong".
OD	To overdose with drugs. To take a lethal quantity of drugs accidentally, or deliberately requiring emergency treatment at a hospital.
PAD	Where you live.
PAKI-BLACK	Cannabis originating in Pakistan.
PEYOTE BUTTONS	Peyote, a hallucinogen.
PHY	Physeptone. Used medically to withdraw addicts from heroin.
PIG	A Garda Officer.
PILLS	Tablets.
PILL HEAD	A user of tablets.
POLLEN	Moroccan Cannabis which is dust like.
POT	Cannabis.
POPPING	Taking tablets.
PUSHER	Seller of Drugs.
PARANOIA	A constant anxiety or fear and suspicion of others.
RIP OFF	Rob.
RITALIN	Ritalin (Amphetamine).
ROLLED-UP	Hand rolled cannabis "joint" (cigarette).

SCENE	Where "it" is happening. The environment, culture, and places where drug users congregate, meet.
SCORE	To get or purchase drugs, cop, do a run.
SCRATCHER	Bed.
SCRIPT	A medical prescription.
SKIN	Cigarette paper for rolling cannabis "joints". Skin up — to hand roll a cannabis "joint" (cigarette).
SKIN POP	To inject under the skin surface.
SHOOT UP	To inject oneself.
SMACK	Heroin.
SMOKE	Cannabis.
SNIFF, SNORT	To sniff cocaine, glue.
SNOW	Cocaine.
SHIT	Cannabis, drugs in general. Also heroin.
SPEEDBALL	Cocaine combined with opiates.
SPIKE	Hypodermic needle.
SPLIT	To leave.
SPEED	Stimulants, Amphetamines, Cocaine.
STASH	To hide drugs.
STICK	Stick of cannabis.
STONED	Highly intoxicated with drugs.

STRAIGHT	Conventional person who doesn't use drugs.
STRUNG OUT	Addicted.
STUFF	Drugs.
SLEEPERS	Sleeping Tablets.
SUGAR	L.S.D.
SUNSHINE	Type of L.S.D.
SUSS	Explore the situation. Find out what's going on (to suss out).
SWEETS	Amphetamines.
SPACED OUT	Obvious signs of effects of drugs or person who is barely in contact with his surroundings.
TAB	L.S.D. Tablet.
TASTE	Using a small quantity of a drug.
TRIP	An L.S.D. experience.
TUNES, TUIES	Tuinal.
TURN ON	To take drugs. Get a "fix".
USER	User of opiates and other drugs.
UPTIGHT	Anxious, upset, angry.
UPPERS	Stimulants, Pep Pills.
VIBES	The vibration a person gives off. Indications of his mood

or attitude.

WEED	Cannabis (Marijuana).
WORKS	Hypodermic syringe with needle.
WRAP UP	Cannabis in metal foil wrapping.

YELLOW BOMBERS,
AND YELLOWS,
YELLOW JACKETS Nembutal.

Appendix 6
The Addict's Problems:
An American View

The rationale behind the Coolemine Lodge approach given by the American psychiatrist, Dr. D. Casriel, in relation to Daytop Village, TC, an affiliate of Coolemine Lodge, explains something of the addict and his problem.

"In general, behaviour is designed to avoid pain and gain pleasure. The adaptive responses in situations of danger (which is anticipation of pain) is either flight and/or fight. Flight is integrated through a perception of danger: the emotion of rage, and the intent to destroy the source of danger. This theory is fine as far as it goes. But it fails to show that there is a third major defence mechanism used to cope with the anticipation of danger or pain. This mechanism is neither fight nor flight. It uses neither the emotions of fear nor rage and may be called detachment, using the non-painful 'emotion' of withdrawal. Just as a turtle puts his head into a shell, so do some people withdraw from the pain of awareness, the pain of reality. It is now theorized that *those people whose primary mechanism of defense is detachment are those who fit into the psychiatric classification of character disorder.* By successfully removing themselves from the pain of reacting to stress, they have spent their energy reinforcing, by encapsulation, their isolation into a nonpainful state of functioning. Once patterned and ingrained, however, detachment very frequently becomes an intrapsychic fortress of one's own making. The patient has taken flight without fear into a fortress in which he feels secure, but in which, realistically, he is quite isolated, incapacitated, and imprisoned. His original fortress has become a stockade. The longer the individual stays in his own jail, the thicker the walls become through secondary encapsulation, with the result that the individual becomes less and less able to cope with the problems of everyday living."

Basic Personality Types

Level of personality integration	Psychotic	Neurotic	Character Disorder
Adult	Psychotherapy with psycho-pharmacology	Reconstructive analytic therapy	Classical forms of treatment relatively ineffective.
Adolescent	,,	Perhaps recon-structive therapy	,,
Childlike	,,	Reparative therapy	,,
Infantile	,,	Supportive therapy	,,

"Once this intrapsychic world with relatively little tension is evolved, the individual will overtly or covertly fight anyone who attempts to remove him from his prison-fortress, from his encapsulated shell of detachment. Once the adaptional mechanism of withdrawal and detachment is solidified and operates as a primary mechanism, the standard psychoanalytic techniques using introspection and observation are useless. The individual patient, though he hears, cannot be reached. Though he knows, he will not change. He will avoid the truth without outright lies. Though he may pay lip service to treatment, he spends conscious and/or unconscious psychic energy in reinforcing his defensive detachment by a secondary encapsulation. Usually pleasurable, the encapsulative shell can be made out of alcohol, drugs, narcotics, delinquency, or just a quiet emotional detachment from all meaningful emotional relationships without necessarily being asocial or antisocial. The detached person tends to identify with people who have similar shells. This gives him pleasurable reassurance with reinforcement.

"If we forcefully remove one means of encapsulation — one shell — such as heroin, the individual will seek a substitute encapsulation such as barbiturates or alcohol.

"A distinction should be made at this point between a neurosis and a character disorder. Feelings such as fear, anger, guilt, and depression are painful to experience and therefore motivate the affected person to ameliorate the pain. These feelings may become so painful that they will prevent the neurotic person from functioning; but even if rendered helpless, the person remains in tremendous pain. This is the situation of the neurotic. Like a person with a toothache, he seeks professional commands to alleviate the pain. The person with a character disorder, however, may feel no pain. Although his teeth or personality are in a state of decay, and although he runs the risk of losing all his teeth, or all his functioning, he does not race to the professional, be it doctor or dentist, and frequently, when forced to go for an appointment others have made for him, he fails to keep it. He knows his teeth are bad, and he also knows he should go to the dentist, but he fears the dentist will hurt and he knows his teeth don't hurt at the moment. He uses all kinds of rationalizations and excuses for not going to the dentist. Like people with rotten teeth, those with character disorders, especially drug addicts, have little if any internal motivation to seek help. This is what we, as professionals, have been up against in the treatment of the character disorder, and the problem is how these patients can be treated efficiently through a psychotherapeutic process. The more completely the mechanisms of primary detachment and secondary encapsulation are employed, the more immature and defective is the emotional level and the personality development. A human personality, like a flower, cannot grow in a closed box. When an individual utilizes withdrawal early in life, or, even in later life, uses emotional detachment as a total defence mechanism, his character stops growing, regresses, and atrophies.

"The problem in treatment becomes obvious.

One must first remove the encapsulating shell, and thereafter prevent the individual from withdrawing into detachment by acquiring any other kind of encapsulating shell. Then, once exposed to the light of reality, powerless to isolate himself, without his fortress-prison-stockade of encapsulation, he is in a position to be taught how to grow up. For the primary addict — those to whom drug addiction is a complete way of life — a full-time institutional therapeutic environment must be utilized to enable the individual to grow up and develop emotionally, socially, culturally, ethically, morally, sexually, and vocationally. This is no small undertaking, but nothing less will suffice. These principles underline our efforts and our treatment techniques at Daytop Village.

"Empirical observation and research at Daytop Village have shown that there are only two simple proscriptions needed for adequate treatment: (1) no physical violence; (2) no narcotics or other chemicals, and, by inference, no outer shells under which to hide. By these two simple prohibitions we have successfully eliminated fight and withdrawal, two of the three ways an individual copes with pain or danger. There is only one avenue left open to him, only one reaction, only one mechanism of defense which he can utilize, and that is by reacting to real and imagined stresses and strains, real and imagined pains and dangers — by fear.

"Motivated by fear, the addict can do one of two things. He can stay at Daytop Village and attempt to cope with his fears, or he can run out of the door, sometimes never to return, frequently to return again at some later date.

"Why does the addict voluntarily stay at Daytop Village? The answer is the genuine love and responsible concern shown to the entering members by the residents. Even though the identification in Freudian terms is that of a narcissistic object type, the addicts stay long enough to develop healthier bonds such as anaclitic identification, and, finally, a positive transference to the Daytop Village community."

Daytop, Daniel Casriel M.D. and Grover Amen, Hill and Wang, New York.

Another Ward River Bestseller!

PAPERFACTS 1

Your Rights as an Irish Citizen

Irish Association of Civil Liberty

guaranteed
irish

Another Ward River Bestseller!

PAPERFACTS 4

Your New House

Patrick J. Kirby

guaranteed
irish

PAPERFACTS 6

Guide for the Disabled

Richard Mooney

guaranteed irish

Dr Rynne's Smoking is your Decision

**The plain facts about smoking
and a sympathetic guide to quitting
written by an Irish family doctor**